A Rosetta / Flowers Joint Production

"This is the most complete, focused and subversive psychedelic resource list in print." - Terence McKenna

"A total jewel of a resource book"
- Alexander Shulgin

ACKNOWLEDGMENTS

Wayne for hypertext manipulation, Steve for data transmutation, Jonny B. for cover glorification, Michael H. for invaluable information, D.M. Turner for inspiration, Mr. Q-Bert and the Bobsy twins for cover augmentation, Cheryl for love and understanding, Forbidden Donut for his Internet expertise, Richard for the original 5-minute flash, Michael M. - initial grist for the mill, Micro Dot, Steven St. James, Erika, Domineditrix for copy editing and Sam Pedro for internal layout and design . . . also thanks to Dover Editions for many of the internal graphics, and finally Jon Hanna, who was a constant source of solace and understanding during the long and sometimes frustrating process of compiling this directory - he is not only great competition but a good friend.

DISCLAIMER

For those interested in update listings, send $1 to get the
latest update or request it free with any order from Rosetta Books.
Updates will begin late 1997.

Rosetta P.O. Box 4611 Berkeley, CA 94704-0611

Cover based on original work by John Barley / Nowsville Communications, E mail: Nowsville@aol.com

Published September 1996 By Rosetta/ Flowers Joint Productions

COPYRIGHT © 1996 BY PHANEROTHYME PRESS ALL RIGHTS RESERVED

The Psychedelic Sourcebook

Distributed by :

Rosetta Wholesale
Fax: (510) 595-3779
P.O. Box 4611 Berkeley, CA 94704-0611 USA

Canada: Hemp B.C., tel: (800) 330-4367, fax: (604) 669-9038

Netherlands: Sensi Seed b.v. tel: (010) 477-3033, fax: (010) 477-8893

Norway: Scorpius Imports, tel: (47) 223-740-41, fax: (47) 223-731-36

United Kingdom: Avalon, tel: (01)705-293-673, fax: (01) 705-780-444
AK, tel: (01)131-555-5165, fax: (01)131-555-5215

Retail credit card orders domestic or international contact:
FS Books @ (800)635-8883 or Mind Books @ (800)829-8127

FOREWORD

Welcome into contact with the *Psychedelic Sourcebook*. The *Sourcebook* is a resource guide to businesses and organizations involved in entheogens.

The catalog or publication of every business listed here has been carefully read through. Many businesses have had orders placed with them to ascertain the quality of their products and services. When service was slow, a note has been made of it in the listing. Most of the listings are my own opinion; I do not simply parrot the companies' own descriptions of themselves from their catalog.

The *Sourcebook* has very few listings related to *Cannabis*, there are enough publications and organizations devoted to it.

The *Sourcebook* does not list head shops. Many years ago, head shops were interesting outposts in the bleak retail landscape. Today, in my home town at least, they are little more than purveyors of sanitized trinkets of no consequence to anyone, especially the serious student of entheogens.

The *Sourcebook* does not accept advertising so as to maintain objectivity about the businesses it reviews.

Rosetta does not sell or trade its mailing list - your confidentiality is assured. Many businesses do sell or trade their lists; if you do not want your name included on these lists, be sure and state this when contacting any of the businesses herein - even if you are just requesting their catalog.

Do not contact any of the botanical companies listed here with questions regarding the pharmacology of their plants. They do not appreciate such inquiries and will not respond to questions concerning the preparation or ingestion of their plants as sacraments.

The *Sourcebook* will bring you into contact with some very interesting resources. There are some good organizations out there. Some are involved in funding research on psychedelics, others are disseminating needed information on their use. I hope you will consider becoming a member of one of these groups - they derive much of their revenue from membership dues.

Exploration of consciousness is one of the most important and rewarding pursuits we can engage in. Psychedelics are a precious tool for doing the deep inner work that needs to occur within all of us. Too many people are running around trying to change the world without first changing themselves. It is a lot easier to project our need for change out onto society than to accept responsibility for the fundamental changes that need to occur within. If the *Sourcebook* can help in some small way to facilitate your personal exploration and growth, then my work has all been worthwhile.

All The Best,

Will Beifuss

ROSETTA

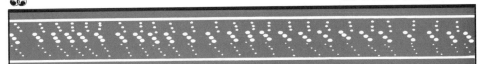

Spores are presently legal for sale because they contain no psilocybin (except in CA where possession or sale of spores from Psychoactive species is illegal). **Spores cannot be shipped to CA.** *I believe that over the next few years the sale of spores from controlled species of mushrooms will be banned in additional states. Some companies have already stopped selling spores to avoid any liability problems.*

Amazing Nature

P.O. Box 318 Dept. R
6500 AH Nijmegen
The Netherlands

Phone: ++31 24 3780573

E-mail: a_nature@telbyte.nl

Free Catalog (available in English, Dutch, German or Spanish)

Sporeprints

Psilocybe cubensis - $33
Psilocybe cyanescens - $40

Home Grow Set - "Finest quality mycelium. Everything you need to harvest between 250-400 gm *P. cubensis* mushrooms." $115.50

All prices include shipping.

Make payment in U.S. dollars (cash) and send by registered mail. See listing under "Botanicals" for additional products.

Florida Mycology Research Center

P.O. Box 8104 Dept. R
Pensacola, FL 32505

904-327-4378

$10 Catalog

They offer 5 catalogs, a "Main" catalog and a "Red" catalog, "Book Store," "Plant Tissue Culture," and the "Chromatograph Buyers Guide" . Catalogs are $10/ea., two for $15, three for $20 or all five for $30. The Main catalog lists growing supplies and edible mushroom spores and cultures; the Red catalog lists the spores and live cultures for many types of mushrooms: both edible, poisonous and psychoactive; the Book Store lists all the books and videos; the Plant Tissue Culture lists supplies for conducting your own sterile plant tissue cultures (this is a method of producing whole plants from tiny pieces of tissue); the Chromatograph Buyers Guide lists the supplies needed to make extractions from mushrooms using the Column Chromatograph method . They also publish *The Mushroom Culture*, a quarterly newsletter of the Independent Mushroom Growers Network, see listing under "Magazines." Membership in the Independent Mushroom Growers Network is $125 and is discussed in further detail in the magazine section.

This company used to sell spores and cultures of psychoactive species to the general public, but they have now restricted the sale of over 130 of these species. These spores are only sold to colleges and universities, mycology businesses and IMGN members. They are doing this in an effort to keep the sale of spores legal by containing them within the mycology research community.

Fungi Perfecti

P.O. Box 7634 Dept. R
Olympia, WA 98507

(360) 426-9292
(800) 780-9126 - Orders

Website:http://www.halcyon. com/mycomed/fppage.html

E-Mail: mycomedia@aol.com

$3 Catalog + $1.44 S&H

Professional catalog with an extensive list of growing supplies, books, spawn and cultures. They do not carry any psychoactive strains of mushrooms, but their catalog is worth getting for the large selection of supplies offered.

Continued on next page...

"Who sees all beings in his own Self, and his own Self in all beings, loses all fear"-
Isa Upanishad

The owner of this company, Paul Stamets, is the author of *The Mushroom Cultivator*, and *Growing Gourmet and Medicinal Mushrooms*, two of the best books written on the subject of mushroom cultivation. His newest book entitled *Psilocybin Mushrooms Of The World: An Identification Guide*, was published in Sept. 1996.

Fungi Perfecti also offers mushroom cultivation workshops 4 times a year at their facility in Olympia, WA. These courses are taught by Paul Stamets and cost $500. One master seminar is offered each year for advanced work and costs $1000. Participants in the basic workshop receive 7 cultures of gourmet mushrooms. Master seminar participants receive 25 cultures.

Homestead Book Co.

P.O. Box 31608 Dept. R
Seattle, WA 98103

Orders 800-426-6777
Questions 206-782-4532

Free Price List
Prices Include Shipping

Mushroom Kit - $70
P. cubensis Spore Print - $25
Mushroom Growing Magic video - $89

Homestead has been marketing their mushroom kit for 20 years now. The problem with many kits is they make it sound like growing mushrooms is a simple task that anyone can do with no effort - and it isn't. If you buy their kit you should also buy one of the mushroom growing books listed under "Suggested Reading" in the back of this *Sourcebook*. They also sell books on mushroom cultivation and marijuana - see their listing under "Books and Catalogs."

JLF

P.O. Box 184 Dept. R
Elizabethtown, IN 47232
812-379-2508

$2 Catalog

P. cubensis spore print - $15
Mushroom spawn grow kit - $40

LER

P.O. Box 1676 Dept. R
Coconut Grove, FL 33233

(305) 649-9997

Website: http://www. shadow.net/~heruka

$3 Catalog

Credit card orders accepted

P. cubensis spore print - $15

IPOMOEA
violacea
Linnaeus

Mika Drake

351 Pleasant St., Box 239 Dept. R
Northampton, MA 01060

Free Catalog
Prices include shipping.

Mika Drake employs the same mushroom growing method that Psylocybe Fanaticus created and popularized. They even use the pictures from the Psylocybe Fanaticus brochure in their price sheet - talk about blatant. Both companies sell spore syringes and instructions, although Mika Drake charges $20 for his instructions which is twice the price of P.F. Unlike P.F., this company sells kits which consist of jars filled with growing medium that have been sterilized and are ready to be inoculated. I don't think these kits are worth the extra cost because it is quite easy to mix up the growing medium yourself—but if you want this work done for you, then these kits would be useful.

Spore syringes - $10/ea + $1 S&H/ea

Substrate formula - $20 - Instructions for making and sterilizing your own growing medium.

Kit 1 - $65 - 10 jars filled with sterilized growing medium, a spore syringe and instructions. They claim it will produce 1 to 2-oz of dried *P. cubensis* mushrooms.

Kit 2 - $363 - 60 jars ready to inoculate. Will produce 10-12 oz of dried mushrooms.

MushroomPeople

560 Farm Rd. P.O. Box 220 Dept. R
Summertown, TN 39493-0220

(800) 386-4495
(615) 964-2200

E-Mail: mushroom@
thefarm.org

Free Catalog

They do not sell spores of any psychoactive mushrooms, but they do sell supplies for mushroom cultivation, from petri dishes to malt agar to pressure cookers. Also a large selection of books on cultivation, field identification and medicinal properties of mushrooms. See their listing under "Book Catalogs."

Mycelium Fruits

P.O. Box 551 Dept. R
Iron Station, NC 28080-0551

$2 Catalog

Sells petri dish cultures, grain spawn masters and plug spawn of edible mushrooms - no psychoactive strains. Also sells some mushroom growing supplies - agar media, petri dishes, spawn bags, pressure cookers, etc.

Myco-Tech

P.O. Box 4647 Dept. R
Seattle, WA 98104

206-364-4851

Free Catalog

P. cubensis Spores, Early strain - $24.95 + $3 S&H
P. cubensis Spores, Amazon strain - $24.95 + $3 S&H
Mushroom kit - $49.95 +$5 S&H
10 lb mushroom kit - $64.95 + $8 S&H
2 lbs pasteurized compost - $24.95 + $5 S&H
10 lbs pasteurized compost - $49.95 + $8 S&H
Book - P. cubensis Aquarium Gardening - $10 + $2 S&H

Myco-Tech sells their spores on a swab inside a sterile test tube. You get a second test tube containing rye grain that is pre-pasteurized. The kits include spores (Earle strain), two pounds of pasteurized compost (straw, cow manure, plus additional ingredients), growing chamber (plastic bag with built in air fil-

ter) and instructions. The 10 lb kits contains 10 lbs of compost. Their catalog states it will take 4-6 weeks to grow mushrooms and that you will get several flushes before the nutrients in the compost are depleted.

Pacific Exotic Spora

P.O. Box 11611 Dept. R
Honolulu, HI 96828

$2 Catalog

This is a reliable company with good quality spores. Their prices are high, but they are one of the only sources of spores for species besides P. cubensis. Their P. cubensis strain is the most expensive on the market, but it does produce very rhizomorphic mycelial growth, which leads to good fruiting ability. They offer:

Spore Prints

Hawaiian *Copelandia cyanescens* spores - $55
P. cubensis (Amazon strain) - $55
P. cubensis (Tasmanian strain) - write for price.
Psilocybe Tampanensis - $125

Psylocybe Fanaticus

1202 E. Pike #783 Dept. R
Seattle, WA 98122

E-mail: pf@pf.seanet.com

$2 Catalog+SASE
Prices include shipping

Spore Syringe - $10/ea
Growing Instructions - $10

This company has developed the easiest method for mushroom growing. You won't need a sterile glove box or have to worry about contamination to nearly the degree of other methods. The problem is low yield, you will not grow as many mushrooms with their technique as you will with conventional methods; this method will only realistically provide enough for personal use. If you have never grown mushrooms before and want to invest in the minimum amount of equipment, then this is a good technique to start with. All you will need is a small pressure canner or micro-

Continued on next page...

"Ministers say that they teach charity. That is natural. They live on handouts. All beggars teach that others should give." - Robert Ingersoll

wave oven, canning jars, and a 10 gallon aquarium or plexiglass to build an equivalent container. Psylocybe Fanaticus sells spore syringes, which are 10cc syringes filled with spores and water. One syringe will inoculate ten 1/2 pint jars which is plenty to get you started. The growing instructions are accurate and easy to follow.

The ShroomKing
**P.O. Box 17444 Dept. R
Seattle, WA 98107**

4 spore syringes and instructions - $30.

Here is another company that has adopted the Psylocybe Fanaticus technique. The ShroomKing, however, is cheaper by $20 - four spore syringes and instructions would cost you $50 from Psylocybe Fanaticus. The ShroomKing does not sell spore syringes individually, so if you only want one syringe - enough to inoculate ten 1/2 pint jars which is enough to get you started - it would be cheaper to buy one from Psylocybe Fanaticus.

Syzygy
**P.O. Box 619 Dept. R
Honaunau, HI 96726**

No Catalog

Psilocybe cubensis spore print - $15 + $1 S&H
Psilocybe azurescens spores - $25 + $1 S&H

Syzygy provides one of the least expensive and best quality *P. cubensis* spore prints. The newly identified *P. azurescens* species is described as more potent, mellower, easy to grow on wood outdoors, and native to the Northwest.

Teonanácatl
**(Postlagernd)
Postamt 1092 Wien Dept. R
A-1092 Vienna
Austria**

Send cash only

Psilocybe cyanescens Astoria Ossip
Small spore sample - $5
Complete spore print - $10 (sm), $20 (lg)

Distributes spores of *Psilocybe cyanescens* Astoria Ossip. This is believed to be the same species as *psilocybe azurescens* and *P. astoriensis*, and is among the most potent of any known species. This is a cold weather fruiting species that grows on wood chips (not rye grain). It grows as big as *Psilocybe cubensis* and is very easy to grow outdoors in a natural culture. These cultures are perennial and can be doubled in size each year without the need for fresh spawn.

"It's interesting to speculate how it developed that in two of the most antifeminist institutions, the church and the law court, the men are wearing the dresses." - Flo Kennedy

Basement Shaman

P.O. Box 1255 Dept. R
Elgin, IL   60121

**E-mail: bshaman@in
teraccess.com**

Catalog $2

If you send this company a spore print, they will do all the lab work for you. They can germinate spores from almost any species and they ask that you not identify your spore print if it is from a controlled species. From their catalog: "Send us your spore print, and in our lab we will germinate your spores under sterile conditions on petri dishes of malt extract agar with antibiotic supplementation. We carefully screen for contaminants and select areas of mycelia which show the most robust, contaminant-free growth. These areas of 'select' growth are introduced to a new set of petri dishes, allowed to incubate, and a second generation of the most desirable mycelia is chosen. Once again, these 'select' colonies are introduced to a new set of petri dishes and grown out. You receive the 5 most promising strains among this 3rd generation, and are guaranteed pure and vigorous cultures. Each petri dish can be used to inoculate up to 10 quart jars of rye grain media." Complete lab services- $85 + $8.50 for 2nd day express shipping.

Bio-Visions

P.O. Box 2767 - Suite 110 Dept. R
Jackson, TN 38302

$1 Catalog

This company offers services similar to the Basement Shaman. They are:

Procedure One - 3 petri dishes inoculated with your spore print. - $24.

Procedure Two - 3 petri dishes containing antibiotic agar are inoculated with your spore print. Promising areas of growth are transferred to a new set of petri dishes. Your spore print returned with 3 inoculated petri dishes. This method is recommended if you suspect your spore print might contain contaminants - $48.

Procedure Three - 3 petri dishes inoculated with your spore print; once areas of growth appear they are transferred to 3 new petri dishes. The most vigorous growth from this second set of dishes is then transferred to 3 new petri dishes. This results in very vigorous cultures from your spores, ready to be used to inoculate rye grain - $105.

Spawn Production - You will receive mason jars that contain mycelium grown on rye grain from your original petri dish cultures. All that is left to do is case the jars with soil and you will have your first flush of mushrooms, 6 jars- $150, 12 jars - $240.

Multiplication of Spawn - You can use each of the above jars of rye grain spawn to inoculate a cubic ft. of pasteurized wheat straw, thus increasing your yield of mushrooms. One cubic ft. of wheat straw with casing soil - $32.

"He that conceals his grief finds no remedy for it" - Turkish proverb

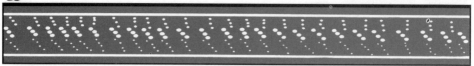

Ace

1643 Lee Rd. #9 Dept. R
Cleveland Hts, OH 44118

(800) 446-4962

Free Catalog

Dr. Timothy Leary

Info-Psychology: A Users Manual for the Human Nervous System - $12.95

Neuro-Politique - $12.95

What Does WoMan Want? (Hardbound-Novel) - $ 9.95

Flashbacks (an autobiography) - $15.95

The Politics of Ecstasy - $12.95

Terence McKenna

The Archaic Revival: Hallucinogens and "The Planet Soul" - $14

Food of the Gods: Search for the Original Tree of Knowledge - $14

True Hallucinations: Extraordinary Adventures in the Devil's Paradise - $12

The Invisible Landscape: Mind, Hallucinogens, and the I Ching - $14

Various Authors

The Doors of Perception and Heaven and Hell - Aldous Huxley - $10

Haight Ashbury Flashbacks - S. Gaskin -$9.95

Insight/Outlook - Albert Hofmann -$10.95

Pharmacotheon - Jonathan Ott - $36.95

Storming Heaven: LSD and The American Dream - Jay Stevens - $13

Andrew Sclanders

11 Albany Rd. Dept. R
Stroud Green
London N4 4RR England

Sells out of print books and a few new titles as well. If you can't find what you are looking for from Flashback Books, Mycophile Books or Red House Books, this is your next best place to try.

Atomic Books

229 West Read St. Dept. R
Baltimore, MD 21201

(410) 728-5490

Website: http://www. atomicbooks.com

$3 Catalog

About 35 titles related to psychedelics. They have separate sections for Timothy Leary and Terence McKenna. You can purchase individual issues of the following magazines: *Psychedelic Illuminations*, *Psychedelic Island Views* (the newsletter of Island Group), *PlantWise* (the newsletter of Botanical Dimensions) and *MAPS* (the magazine of the Multidisciplinary Association for Psychedelic Studies).

Avalon

73 Fawcett RD.
Southsea, Hants
PO4 0BB ENGLAND

011 44-1-705-293-673
Fax 011 44-1-705-780-444

A good source for publications on *Cannabis* and entheogenic information in the U.K., where this information can be hard to find. They sell both wholesale and retail.

Basement Shaman

P.O. Box 1255 Dept. R
Elgin, IL 60121

E-mail: bshaman @interaccess.com

$2 Catalog

A small but good selection of books including:

A Druid's Herbal for the Sacred Earth - $12.95

Amazonia by Richard E. Schultes - $22.95

Ayahuasca Visions: The Religious Iconography of a Peruvian Shaman by Luis Eduardo Luna and Pablo Amaringo - $60

Ayahuasca Analogues - Pangaean Entheogens by Jonathan Ott - $15 paper back, $30 clothbound

"It really is a wonderful thing to merely write a letter and get some rare treasure that grows in some distant part of the world." - Harry Saier

Eduardo el Curandero - The Words of a Peruvian Healer - $8 paperback

Pharmacotheon: by Jonathan Ott $40 softcover, $70 hard cover

Pharmako/Poeia by Dale Pendell - $16.95

Plant Spirit Medicine by Eliot Cowan - $14.95

Plants of the Gods by Richard E. Schultes - $19.95 softcover

Psychedelic Shamanism by Jim Dekorne - $19.95 softcover

Rio Tigre and Beyond: The Amazon Jungle Medicine of Manuel Cordova by F. Bruce Lamb - $15 paperback

Satsun: My Apprenticeship with a Maya Healer by Rosita Arvigo - $22.50 softcover

Tales of a Shaman's Apprentice by Mark Plotkin - $14.95 softcover

The Age of Entheogens & The Angels' Dictionary by Jonathan Ott - $16.95 softcover

The Archaic Revival by Terence McKenna - $14

The Cacahuatl Eater: Ruminations of an Unabashed Chocolate Addict by Jonathan Ott - $20 hardcover

The Invisible Landscape by Terence McKenna - $14 softcover

The Sacred Mushroom Seeker: Essays For R. Gordon Wasson - ed. by Thomas Riedlinger - $38

True Hallucinations by Terence McKenna - $12 softcover

Vine of The Soul: Medicine Men, Their Plants and Rituals in the Columbian Amazonia by Richard E. Schultes - $22.95 softcover.

Wizard of the Upper Amazon: The Story of Manuel Cordova-Rios by F. Bruce Lamb - $13 paperback.

Blue Water Publishing

P.O. Box 726 Dept. R
Newburg, OR 97132
(800) 366-0264

Free Catalog

Mostly a new age bookseller, they are included here because they sell Terence McKenna's books and tapes.

Books by McKenna

The Invisible Landscape - $14

The Archaic Revival - $14

Food of the Gods - $14.95

True Hallucinations - $12

Trialogues at the Edge of the West - $12

Flashback Books

40 Fourth St., Suite 260 Dept. R
Petaluma, CA 94952

707-762-4714

$5 - Catalog #9

$5 - Catalog #8
(limited copies remain)

$5 - *Lysergic World* (1993)

$15 - *Shaman Woman, Mainline Lady: Women's Writings on the Drug Experience* (1982). Large trade pub. Also available hardback for $25.

Flashback Books is a mail-order firm specializing in rare and out-of-print books on psychedelics, ethnobotany and the '60s counterculture. Catalog 9 offers about 500 books for sale, about half on psychedelics and sacred plants, and half drug novels and memoirs. There are also some rare R. Gordon Wasson titles available.

This is an excellent catalog. The annotated entries make great reading and offer an invaluable glimpse back to an important and formative time in our history. Highly recommended.

Also available is *Lysergic World*, a 16pp tabloid-style publication produced in April 1993 to coincide with the celebration of the 50th anniversary of the discovery of LSD. There is an excellent chronology of the history of LSD, a centerfold world map in color showing historic sites of LSD discovery, research and culture; articles on LSD's impact on science, religion, and the CIA; lists of LSD in songs, film and books, original contributions by Hofmann and Leary, and more. Highly recommended.

Shaman Woman, Mainline Lady, 285pp, 130 illustrations. The only anthology devoted to women's writings on the drug experience, from the early Victorians through the 1970s.

Michael Horowitz, the man behind Flashback Books, was the founder-director of the Fitz Hugh Ludlow Memorial Library, one of the world's finest collections of rare drug books, manuscripts, art and artifacts (but unfortunately in storage for more than a decade and thus unavailable for use).

FS Book Co.
P.O. Box 417457 Dept. R
Sacramento, CA 95841-7457

916-725-0341

$3 Catalog

 Over 30 titles on marijuana cultivation and use, and over 20 titles on mushroom growing and identification. They also carry a number of books on psychedelics including those by Terence McKenna, Jonathan Ott and D.M. Turner's excellent *The Essential Psychedelic Guide*. They have a series of 14 booklets on marijuana cultivation and drug manufacturing for $32 a set. Some booklet titles in this series are *The Psilocybin Producers Guide*, *Peyote and other Psychoactive Cacti*, *D.M.T. Guide* and *Home Grown Highs*. The FS Book Company no longer sells mushroom spores.

The Headshop
Kloveniersburgwal 39 Dept. R
1011 JW Amsterdam, Holland

31-20-624-9061
Fax 31-20-620-8250

This place is what headshops were meant to be, paraphernalia heaven. They carry a large number of books on *Cannabis* and psychedelics from around the world. A great place to smoke a "J" and figure out what to do next...

Hemp B.C.
21 Water St. Dept. R
Vancouver, B.C. Canada V6B 1A1

800-330-4397
Fax 604-669-9038

A very political outfit that is pushing the envelope in terms of *Cannabis* laws in Canada. They were recently busted for selling *Cannabis* seed, not that has stopped them (no deliveries to the USA of seed). Large selection of books on mushrooms, psychedelics and *Cannabis*. They do sell mail order.

Homestead Book Co.
P.O. Box 31608
Seattle, WA 98103

Orders: (800) 426-6777
Questions: (206) 782-4532

Free Price List

A small selection of books, 13 titles, on mushroom cultivation and field identification, and marijuana growing. They also sell *P. cubensis* spores and mushroom kits, see their listing under "Spores and Kits."

Island Group
1803 Mission St., Suite 175 Dept. R
Santa Cruz, CA 95060

(408) 427-1942

E-mail: bruce@ mindmedia.com
Website: http:// www.island.org

Free Catalog

The Island Group is "A free association of individuals dedicated to the creation of a psychedelic culture." Although they are a membership organization (see their listing under "Organizations"), you do not need to be a member to order from their catalog of books and tapes.

Books Available

Chaos and Cyberculture by Leary, 1994 - $24.95

High Priest by Timothy Leary - $19.95

Ecstasy: The MDMA Story, 2nd Ed. by Bruce Eisner 1994, signed by author - $17.95

Island by Aldous Huxley - $7

Huxley in Hollywood by David King Dunaway, 1989 - $24.95

Shaman Woman, Mainline Lady: Women's Writing on the Drug Experience - edited by Michael Horowitz, 1984 - $15

Psychedelics Encyclopedia - 3rd Edition by Peter Stafford, 1992 - $29.95

PIHKAL : A Chemical Love Story by Alexander and Ann Shulgin, 1991 - $18.95

Surfing the Consciousness Nets by Leary - $24.95

Magic Grams by Peter Stafford - $30

Psychedelic Baby Reaches Puberty by Peter Stafford - $30

"Any close and worthwhile contact with the earth tends to make one original, or at least detached in one's judgments and independent of group control." - L.H. Bailey

Jonathan Ott Books

P.O. Box 1251 Dept. R
Occidental, CA 95465

Free Price List
include $3 per book S & H
CA residents add 7.5% tax

The Cacahuatl Eater : Ruminations of an Unabashed Chocolate Addict - $10 paper back, $20 hardcover

Pharmacotheon : Entheogenic Drugs, Their Plant Sources and History - $40 softcover, $70 hardcover

Ayahuasca Analogues : Pangaean Entheogens - $15 paperback, $30 clothbound

The Age of Entheogens & The Angels' Dictionary - $18 paperback, $36 clothbound, $72 signed limited edition

Four of Jonathan's books are available direct from the publisher:

The Cacahuatl Eater : Ruminations of an Unabashed Chocolate Addict - published in 1985, this is the first book to treat chocolate first and foremost as a drug, and to suggest the chemical basis for the chocolate habit. Mr. Ott lays to rest the myths of chocolate causing acne, tooth decay, obesity, migraine, allergies, etc. Written in a lighthearted, humorous style, in sharp contrast to the very serious tone of his other three books, *The Cacahuatl Eater* is informative, irreverent and highly recommended. Available in a $10 paperback edition or $20 hardcover, 128 pp, 27 photos.

Pharmacotheon : Entheogenic Drugs, Their Plant Sources and History - is the most comprehensive book on the subject ever written. Ott has extensive personal experience with entheogens which gives his writings the ring of truth. This is particularly evident in his self-experiments with ayahuasca analogues contained in the chapter entitled "Beta-Carbolines and Ayahuasca Potions." The book has 6 chapters and 5 appendices. Chapter 1 - "Mescaline, Péyotl, San Pedro, Artificial Phenethylamines." Chapter 2 - "LSD, Ololiuhqui Kykeon: The Ergoline Complex." Chapter 3 - "DMT, Cohoba, Epená: Short-Acting Tryptamines." Chapter 4 - "Beta-Carbolines and Ayahuasca Potions." Chapter 5 -

"Psilocybine/Psilocine/Baeocystine: The Teonanácatl Complex." Chapter 6 - "Ibotenic Acid/Muscimol: The Primordial Panx and Amita." The 5 appendices are: Sundry Visionary Compounds with 8 mini-chapters; "Putative Entheogenic Species" with annotated lists of lesser-known visionary drugs; "Index of Entheogen Chemistry" with condensed chemical data on the 50 most important entheogenic compounds; "Botanical Index" to more than 1,100 species cited in the text; and "Suggested General Reading" - complement the text and bibliography. This book is essential reading. Available as a $40 softcover or as a $70 hardcover, 640 pp.

Ayahuasca Analogues : Pangaean Entheogens - From the press release: "This is the first book to explore in detail the human pharmacology of ayahuasca, the jungle ambrosia of Amazonia. In the alembic of his own brain, Ott elucidates the basic pharmacology of this rainforest potion via psychonautic experiments with *pharmahuasca* - pure compounds in ayahuasca capsules. He also describes the brewing of ayahuasca-like potions using commercially available temperate-zone plants as sources for the Beta-carbolines and DMT. Ott documents that there are at least 4000 possible combinations of plant infusions which can yield entheogenic potions using technology no more complicated than that employed for making coffee or tea." Available as a $15 paperback, a $30 clothbound edition, or a $60 signed, numbered, limited edition (200 copies) with cloth slipcase, 128 pp.

The Age of Entheogens & The Angels' Dictionary - combines two essays on visionary drugs. *The Age of Entheogens* is a reexamination of the history of our western civilization, exploring the brutal suppression of ecstatic, experiential religions by the 1600-year-old Pharmacratic Inquisition, leading up to the contemporary Entheogenic Reformation, or replacement with *genuine* entheogens of the *placebo* sacraments at the hollow center of today's purely symbolic religions. *The Angel's Dictionary* is a lexicon having 318 words pertaining to sacred inebriants, ecstatic states and kindred topics; with 290 definitions and 445 quo-

Continued on next page...

"The human body is the temple of God. It is the real church, the synagogue, and the mosque made by God." - Kirpal singh

tations from classic drug and general literature.

I sure wish he had included pronunciation information like a dictionary does - there are so many words few of us know for sure how to pronounce! Available as an $18 paperback, $36 clothbound and $72 signed, limited, numbered [126 copies; 1-100, A-Z] edition with clothbound slipcase. [160pp].

Last Gasp
777 Florida St. Dept. R
S.F., CA 94110
(800) 848-4277
Free Quarterly Catalog
$5 Full Catalog

Large catalog with wide selection of alternative titles. Section on drug literature includes some psychedelic titles.

Loompanics Unlimited
P.O. Box 1197 Dept. R
Port Townsend, WA 98368
$5 Catalog

A huge 280 page catalog of controversial and unusual books on a wide variety of subjects. "An important source for anarchists, survivalists, iconoclasts, self-liberators, mercenaries, investigators, dropouts, researchers and just about anyone interested in the strange, the useful, the arcane, the oddball, the unusual, the unique and the diabolical." You will receive quarterly supplements for 1 year with your purchase of the main catalog. Highly recommended.

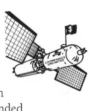

Luna Information Services
6160 Packard St. Dept. R
Los Angeles, CA 90035-2581
(213) 655-5440
$2 Catalog

Magic Mushrooms Around the World - $22.95 + $3 S&H (plus $1.65 tax in CA)

LSD Molecule 50th Anniversary Mug - $12/ ea, $9 ea addl, Set of 6 - $50, postpaid

Shaman Woman, Mainline Lady - $9.75 (235 pp.   softcover, 1982)

LSD Bibliography - $13 + $3.50 S&H (70 pp)

LIS publishes and distributes information related to psychedelics. They carry an LSD bibliography covering the years 1950-1960. Compiled by Dr. Oscar Janiger, it has over 700 citations on 70 pages covering this most prolific period of LSD research. This is a partial list of a complete bibliography Luna expects to have finished later this year. The complete version will have about 5000 entries, representing every scientific article published since the discovery of LSD in 1943. This is a bibliography, it lists the author, title and source of the articles and is not a collection of the articles themselves. Cost of the partial bibliography from the 1950s is $13 plus $3.50 S&H. Purchase of this bibliography entitles you to a copy of the full bibliography, when it is completed, on computer disk at cost (the price of the disk itself and shipping).

Also available is the LSD Molecule 50th Anniversary Mug. This is a 12 oz white ceramic mug with a 3 color imprint. This was produced in 1993 to commemorate the 50th anniversary of the discovery of LSD by Albert Hofmann in 1943. The mug comes with a no-risk guarantee.

LIS is about to publish an English language version of Jochen Gartz's book - *Magic Mushrooms Around the World: A Scientific Journey Across Cultures and Time*. It is the first book on psychoactive mushrooms available in the U.S. for more than 10 years. Originally published in German in 1993, this revised and expanded English language edition is scheduled for re-

"All substances are poisons; there is none which is not a poison. The right dose differentiates a poison and a remedy." - Paracelsus

lease in October 1996. The book explores the psychedelic fungi of 5 continents, and includes: laboratory analysis of active ingredients, new mushroom cultivation techniques, plant growth hormones to accelerate growth, psychotherapy applications, the dangers of accidental poisoning, the bluing phenomenon, history of mushroom usage and much more. 138 pages, 8"x11" sturdy softcover, 30 color illustrations, 40 b& w/ illustrations, $22.95 plus $3 shipping. All pre-publication orders come with a no-risk guarantee - if you are dissatisfied for any reason simply return the book for a full refund. Recommended.

Mind Books

321 S. Main St. #543 Dept. R
Sebastopol, CA 95472

(800) 829-8127
Website: http://www.promind.com

Free Catalog
Credit Card Orders Accepted

Mind Books has put together the finest selection of books of any company listed here. With almost 250 titles in stock, you will discover many books you never knew existed as well as all of the classics. Mind Books catalog is so thorough and complete that I am left speechless. You simply must get this catalog, there will never be a better selection to choose from anywhere. All titles are described quite well, which makes this catalog very readable.

MushroomPeople

560 Farm Rd. P.O. Box 220
Summertown, TN 39493-0220
(800) 386-4495
E-mail: mushroom@thefarm.org

Free Catalog

A large selection of books on mushroom cultivation, field identification, and cooking recipes. Most of these books deal with shiitake, morels, oyster, etc., but some include psychoactive species as well. They also have a section devoted to entheogens with about 30 titles in it; a well chosen selection, not a bad title in the lot.

Mycophile Books

P.O. Box 93 Dept. R
Naples, FL 33939-0093
(813) 262-3363 (Evenings)

$3 Catalog

Specializes in books and periodicals on hallucinogenic drugs and plants. Sells both out-of-print and in-print items and can respond to want lists and orders. They also provide a search service. They sell sheets of blotter acid art - looks just like the real thing, perforations and all - signed by Leary, Shulgin and others. A previous series signed by Albert Hofmann is sold out. Cost is about $200, call or write for a price quote. They carry a number of R. Gordon Wasson's books including:

The Wondrous Mushroom: Mycolatry in Meso-America - $395

Maria Sabina and Her Mazatec Mushroom Velada (includes 4 LPs and a 79 page musical score) - $375

Persephone's Quest: Entheogens and the Origins of Religion - $225

Soma: Divine Mushroom of Immortality - $1095

Panther Press

1032 Irving St., #514 Dept. R
San Francisco, CA 94122
Wholesale inquiries welcome

The Essential Psychedelic Guide - 112 pp pb - $12.95 + $2 S&H (CA residents add .94 tax)

Salvinorin: The Psychedelic Essence of Salvia Divinorum - 58 pp pb - $9.95 + $2 S&H (CA residents add .72 tax)

Salvinorin: The Psychedelic Essence of Salvia Divinorum This is D.M. Turner's new book, Published in August '96. Once again, he is on the cutting edge of research, this time with the rare compound salvinorin A. From the press release:

"The most powerful natural psychedelic known has recently been isolated from a rare Mexican sage, *Salvia divinorum*. The active com-

Continued on next page...

pound, salvinorin A, has astonished users and researchers with its dramatic and intense psychoactive effects, which are quite distinct from those of other psychedelics. Early experiments with salvinorin A have shown diverse results, ranging from alarming intensity and terror, to experiences of exquisite feelings and insights, transformative and healing energies, and bizarre physical/geometric dimensions."

"In the first book dedicated to this subject, D.M. Turner discusses *Salvia divinorum's* botany, history and use by Mazatec Indian shamans in Oaxaca; the discovery by western researchers and subsequent experiments that yielded salvinorin A; methods for using both the extract and whole plant material, and descriptions of *Salvia divinorum's* unique effects."

"Firsthand experiental accounts from pioneering users are presented, along with vivid descriptions of Turner's own extensive journeys within the fascinating and brave new worlds afforded by *Salvia divinorum*."

The Essential Psychedelic Guide

This is such a good book, I insist you buy it because it contains information you will not find anywhere else. The beauty about this book is that it is written from firsthand experience, and the author, D.M. Turner, has had a lot of it. There are chapters on LSD,  Mushrooms, Mescaline, DMT, Ecstasy, 2C-B, Harmala Alkaloids, and Ketamine. Information is given on each drug's effect at various dosages and how the effects compare with the other drugs. A chapter entitled "Multiple Combinations" explores the effects of some very heroic drug amalgamations. For example, Mushrooms + Syrian rue + DMT + Nitrous Oxide + Ketamine, or how about LSD + Syrian rue + DMT + 5-MEO-DMT + Nitrous Oxide + *Cannabis*. These are realms very few people have explored, and D.M. Turner is the first to write about them. There are some natural psychedelics not covered in this book - ayahuasca, ibogaine and natural sources of tryptamines such as *Phalaris* grass. Hopefully a sequel will be written that includes these plant teachers. D.M. Turner's writing style is clear and concise and a real pleasure to read. I cannot recommend this book highly enough!

Psychedelic Illuminations
P.O. Box 3186 Dept. R
Fullerton, CA 92634

(714) 733-1252

Free Book List
$30 for 4 Issues of the magazine

A good selection of books, about 70 titles, all on entheogens. They also sell a few CDs featuring Timothy Leary and John Lilly. Also available is McKenna's Time Wave Zero software. Write them and request their free book list.

Quick Trading Co.
P.O. Box 429477 Dept. R
San Francisco, CA 94142-9477

800-428-7825

$2 Catalog

A small catalog, less than 30 titles, most on marijuana cultivation. Inquire about wholesale if you are in the business. They do carry a few titles on psychedelics, which are:

Psilocybin: Magic Mushroom Growers Guide $16.95

The Essential Psychedelic Guide - $12.95

PIHKAL - $18.95
E for Ecstasy - $19.95

Red House Books

P.O. Box 460267 Dept. R
San Francisco, CA 94146

(415) 282-8933

$2 Catalog

Red House sells first editions and out-of-print books on many subversive and underground topics. They have a section on **Drugs**, a section on **Tim Leary**, and one for **Art Kleps** (of Neo-American Church fame.) Their selection is not nearly as good as Flashback Books, but if you are looking for out of print books, you can't leave any stone unturned. They will do book searches as well.

"I have believed in my convictions and been convicted for my beliefs." - G.S. Heron

Redwood City Seed Co.

P.O. Box 361 Dept. R
Redwood City, CA 94064

(415) 325-7333

Website:
http://www.batnet.com/rwc-seed/shamanic.books.html

"Plants of the Gods" Catalog - Free

They publish a small catalog supplement entitled "Plants of the Gods" that has the following books:

Hallucinogens and Culture by Peter Furst ('76)

The Hippies and American Values by T. Miller

Lame Deer: Seeker of Visions by John Fire Lame Deer ('72)

Plants of the Gods: Their Sacred, Healing and Hallucinogenic Powers by Richard E. Schultes & Albert Hofmann ('79)

Power Music: Music & Trance in the Shamanic Universe by B. Christman ('89)

Man and His Symbols by C.G. Jung ('64)

Narcotic Plants of the Old World ('79)

Psychedelics Encyclopedia by Peter Stafford ('92)

Hallucinogens and Shamanism by Michael Harner ('73)

Ronin Books by Phone

Box 522 Dept. R
Berkeley, CA 94701

(800) 858-2665 - Orders
(510) 548-2124 - Info

$2 Catalog

This is the mail order outlet for Ronin Publishing. They have the following books on psychedelics:

Psychedelics Encyclopedia, P. Stafford - $24.95

Ecstasy: The MDMA Story, B. Eisner - $17.95

Growing the Hallucinogens, H. Grubber - $9.95

Psych. Underground Set (9 booklets) - $22.95

The Politics of Ecstasy, T. Leary - $14.95

The Scientist, John Lilly - $14.95

Haight Ashbury Flashbacks, S. Gaskin - $9.95

They also have a number of titles on marijuana cultivation.

Rosetta

P.O. Box 4611 Dept. R
Berkeley, CA 94704-0611

Wholesale inquiries welcome
Fax us and we'll send you our catalog

Fax (510) 595-3779

$1 or $2 Catalog or Free With Order

This is a great catalog. Their specialty is facsimile copies of out-of-print research papers on psychopharmacology and ethnobotany. Also, they sell facsimile copies of all 10 issues of *The Psychozoic Press,* the forerunner to *Psychedelic Monographs and Essays,* that was published from 1982-84. They also have facsimile copies of all 11 issues of *The Psychedelic Review,* the classic publication of the '60s whose editors include: Alpert, Leary, Metzner, Watts, Ferlingetti and more. They have research papers on such subjects as: Ayahuasca, Ibogaine, Tryptamines, Venoms, Phenethylamines, Peyote, San Pedro, Datura, Khat, Guarana, Kava Kava, Hallucinogens and more. Also Rosetta is the exclusive source for *Notes From Underground, A Gracie and Zarkov Reader,* $12 post paid. Rosetta has expanded their selection of books in their new catalog. They will beat anyone's advertised price on any book. They also sell artwork, a few t-shirts and some good tea blends. This catalog is a must.

Rosetta now distributess wholesale to like business; inquire for prices. Specify wholesale or retail when requesting a catalog.

Rosetta also publishes this *Sourcebook.* For those interested in update listings, send $1 to get the latest update or request it free with any order. Updates will begin late 1997.

Sensi Seed B.V.

P.O. Box 1771 Dept. R
3000 BT Rotterdam
The Netherlands

31-10-477-3033
Fax 31-10-477-8893

Largest distributor of hemp and entheogenic information in Holland. This company sells a complete line of English and foreign language publications. They have stores in both Amsterdam and Rotterdam. They also run the *Cannabis* museum in Amsterdam and the world famous Seed Bank (no deliveries to the USA of seed).

Skyline Books

P.O. Box T Dept. R
Forest Knolls, CA 94933

(415) 488-9491

E-mail: skylinbk@ix.netcom.com
Website: http://www.abaa-booknet.com/
usa/skyline/

Free Catalog

Skyline sells rare and out-of-print books on counterculture, Beat and modern literature. It has a number of titles on drugs, some of which cover psychedelics. They also sell antique medicine bottles which contained ingredients such as *Cannabis* , cocaine, opium and morphine. They also purchase books or accept them on consignment and will do book searches. Catalogs #16 & #17 are available.

Spectral Mindustries

P.O. Box 73401 Dept. R
Davis, CA 95617-3401

E-mail: specmind@aol.com
Website: http://www.cyberverse.com/~
martins/TELR/dossier.html

Sacred Mushrooms and the Law - $5 + $1.50 S&H (CA residents add $.50 tax)

This is a 35 pp. booklet compiled by Richard Glen Boire who publishes *The Entheogen Law Reporter* (see listing under "Magazines and Newsletters.") Some of the info. is from previous issues of *TELR* but rewritten with much new information added. All the federal and state laws concerning *Psilocybe* mushrooms are discussed and explained. Charts display potential punishments under the federal sentencing guidelines. Also includes a state-by-state chart giving the various state punishments for possessing and cultivating mushrooms. Also discusses the legal status of *Amanita muscaria* and the religious defense to criminal charges.

This is a concise, easy to understand source of legal information. If you want to know what the law is regarding mushrooms, their spores and mycelium, this is the place to find it. Recommended.

Sweetlight Books

16625 Heitman Rd. Dept. R
Cottonwood, CA 96022

916-529-5392

E-mail: swtlight@snowcrest.net
Website: http://www.snowcrest.net/swtlight

Free Catalog

A small but good selection of books on peyote and marijuana. They also publish *Holy Smoke*, a magazine for people who use marijuana as a sacrament and medicine. A year's subscription is $20 for 4 issues. Single copies available for $5.

Thaneros Press

P.O. Box 773 Dept. R
Lone Pine, CA 93545

Free Information Sheet

Thanatos To Eros - $17.95 + $3 S&H (CA residents add $1.39 tax)

Thaneros Press published Myron Stolaroff's book *Thanatos To Eros*. Stolaroff founded the International Foundation for Advanced Study which researched the use of LSD and mescaline in psychotherapy in the early '60s. This autobiography details his experiences with psychedelics including MDMA, 2C-B, 2C-T-2, 2C-T-7, 2C-E and others. The book has a foreword by Alexander and Ann Shulgin. Hardcover, 192 pages. Highly recommended. Note: check with Thaneros Press regarding the forthcoming paperback edition, the current hardcover edition is sold out.

"Who will prefer the jingle of jade pendants if he once has heard stone growing in a cliff?" - Tao Tzu

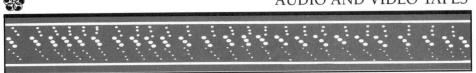

Ace

1643 Lee Rd. #9 Dept. R
Cleveland Hts, OH 44118

(800) 446-4962

Free Catalog

Timothy Leary - Live at Starwood

From Psychedelics to Cybernetics - $9.95

The Inner Frontier
  (with Robert Anton Wilson) - $9.95

How to Operate Your Brain, - $9.95

Terence McKenna -

History Ends in Green (6 tape set) - $39.95

Conversations at the Edge of Magic - $9.95

Rap Dancing into the Third Millenium - $9.95

Packing for the Long Strange Trip - $9.95

Seeking the Stone (video) - $29.95

Alien Dreamtime (video) - $19.98

Basement Shaman

P.O. Box 1255 Dept. R
Elgin, IL 60121

**E-mail: bshaman@
  interaccess.com**

Catalog $2

A full series of tapes from the Botanical Preservation Corps seminars on the Ethnobotany and Chemistry of Sacred Plants presented by the leading thinkers, researchers and explorers in the field. In addition they carry the following tapes:

Audio Tapes by Terence McKenna

Sacred Plants as Guides 1991 - 3 tapes, $32

Plants, Visions and History - $12

Ethnobotany: A Complete Course - 5 tapes, $50

*Understanding and Imagination in the Light of
  Nature* - $12

Having Archaic and Eating it Too - 2 tapes, $18

UFO's: The Inside Outsider - $12

Alien Dreamtime - 60 min. video tape, $20

Timewave Zero - computer software, Mac or
  MS DOS version, $54

Timothy Leary - How to Operate Your Brain
  Video Tape - $24

Other Listings

Peyote Canyon, a Collection of Peyote Songs -
  CD $15.95

*A Tribal Didgeridoo, Collection of Traditional
Aboriginal Didgeridoo Songs* - CD $15.95

Big Sur Tapes

P.O. Box 4-PY Dept. R
Tiburon, CA 94920

800-688-5512

**Website:
  http://www.bigsurtapes.com**

Free Catalog

They have audio tapes of Albert Hofmann, Humphrey Osmond, Aldous Huxley, Timothy Leary, Stanislav Grof, Henry Munn, John Lilly, Prem Das, Ralph Metzner, Andrew Weil, Claudio Naranjo and R. Gordon Wasson, among others. The Wasson tapes were recorded at Esalen in 1975, and to my knowledge are the only tapes available of him. A very good selection of tapes. Recommended.

R. Gordon Wasson Tapes

Magic Mushroom - $11

Maria Sabina - $11

Ancient Entheogenic Images - $11

The Wasson Mushroom Set -
  (the above 3 tapes) $25

"We must not fall into the arrogance of 'human rights' but must realize the importance of Natural Rights." - John Trudell

Blue Water Publishing

P.O. Box 726 Dept. R
Newburg, OR 97132

(800) 366-0264

Free Catalog

Mostly a new age bookseller, their only redeeming value being they sell some McKenna tapes.

Audio Tapes by McKenna

Time Wave, The Tao & Novelty - $10.95

Personal Bio. & Time Wave - $10.95

Time Wave Light - $10.95

Magical Mystery Tour - 2 tapes, $18

Life Tides and Time Lines - 4 tapes, $32

Dynamics of Hyperspace - $10.95

The Voynich Manuscript - $10.95

Alien Love - $10.95

Hot Concepts and Melting Edges - $10.95

The Definitive UFO Tape - $9

New & Old Maps of Hyperspace - $10.95

Magical Mystery Tour - 2 tapes - $18

Software by McKenna

Time Wave Zero
    Mac/Dos Time Surfer - $40
    Dos Time Explorer - $54

Botanical Preservation Corps

Box 1368 Dept. R
Sebastopol, CA 95473

Free Catalog

The BPC organizes seminars and field courses on ethnobotany and chemistry of entheogenic plants. They also sell audio tapes of the talks given at these seminars by some of the most prominent people in the field. Two years ago, the BPC suspended sales of their tapes, but last year they reissued their catalog with some new titles added as well. This is an excellent series of tapes, the speakers tend to be more explicit about information regarding entheogens then they are at seminars held in the U.S. There is a lot of technical information that can be gleaned from these tapes; if you are serious about the history, chemistry and use of entheogens, these tapes are some of the best on the market.

The following tapes were recorded in Jan. 1993 at a BPC field course in Veracruz, Mexico. This is just a partial list:

1. Jonathan Ott: *The Politics and Problems of Drug Policy* - $10

2. J. Ott: *Teonanácatl - Psilocybin Mushrooms-* 2 tapes, $13

3. J. Ott: *Chemistry Lab* - 3 tapes, $20

4. J. Ott: *Ergot, LSD, Ololiuhqui and Lysergic Acid Amides* - 2 tapes, $13

5. J. Ott: *Ayahuasca Analogues* -$10

14. Terence McKenna: *Psychedelics, Evolution and History* - $10

15. T. McKenna: *The Search for DMT in the Amazon* - $10

16. T. McKenna: *What I have learned from Psychedelics* - $10

17. T. McKenna: *Experiment at La Chorrera* - $10

18. T. McKenna: *Ayahuasca* - $10

19. T. McKenna: *The Metaphysics of Psychedelics* - 3 tapes, $23

The following tapes are not part of the '93 Veracruz field course:

24. Dennis McKenna: *Alkaloids and Evolution* - 2 tapes, $13

25. D. McKenna: *The Ayahuasca (Hoasca) Project* - $10

26. Richard Evans Schultes: *Ethnobotany & Rainforest Preservation* - $10

28. Richard Evans Schultes: *Hallucinogenic Plants* - $10

29. Alexander Shulgin: *Neurotransmitters* - $10

30. Alexander Shulgin: *Chemistry Lab* - 2 tapes, $13

The catalog contains a detailed description of all these tapes. Audio tapes of the BPC seminars held in Palenque, Mexico (Jan. '95 and '96) are now available. These tapes feature Jonathan Ott, Terence McKenna, Ralph Metzner, Rob Montgomery, Christian Rätsch, Stacy Schaeffer and Manuel Torres, among others. I have heard this set of tapes as well and they are excellent.

"Question with boldness even the existence of God; because if there be one, He must approve the homage of reason rather than that of blindfolded fear." - Thomas Jefferson

Dolphin Tapes

P.O. Box 71 Dept. R
Big Sur, CA 93920

Free Tape List w/SASE

Dolphin Tapes has no complete catalog, just overlapping tape lists published once or twice a year. They can be slow in filling orders so have patience. They have audio tapes of Aldous Huxley, Timothy Leary, Prem Das, Stanislav Grof, Albert Hofmann, Andrew Weil plus the second largest selection of Terence McKenna tapes. (Sound Photosynthesis has the largest.) Recommended.

Island Group

1803 Mission St., Suite 175 Dept. R
Santa Cruz, CA 95060

(408) 427-1942

**E-mail: bruce@
 mindmedia.com**
Website: http://www.island.org

Free Catalog
$5 shipping regardless of size of order

Sells the following audio and video tapes:

Bicycle Day: The April 16, 1993 proceedings at U.C. Santa Cruz celebrating the 50th anniversary of the discovery of LSD. Presentations by Dr. Oscar Janiger, Dr. Lester Grinspoon, Ralph Abraham, Robert Anton Wilson, Claudio Naranjo, Laura Huxley and others. Includes videotaped messages from Albert Hofmann, Humphrey Osmond, and Ken Kesey. Three-hour video: $30 or three one-hour audio tapes: $19.95.

The Bridge Conference: From the conference on psychedelics held at Stanford University Feb. 2nd & 3rd, 1991. Featuring Timothy Leary, Terence McKenna, John Lilly, Francis Huxley, Peter Stafford, Bruce Eisner and many others. Video $30. (2 hours)

Ecstasy: From Psychotherapy to the Rave Culture 1994: A lecture by Bruce Eisner, author of *Ecstasy: The MDMA Story.* The talk focuses on the new government sanctioned research and the use of MDMA in the rave scene. Includes question and answer period. 90 min. video, $30.

How to Operate Your Brain: Timothy Leary

narrates to computer graphics and sampled music. Includes some excerpts from his album LSD, which came out in 1966. Produced by Retenalogic. Video, $30. (30 min.)

Trance - Formation Session: Timothy Leary at U.C. Santa Cruz, Feb. 16, 1993. The past, present and future of multi-media is explored utilizing the sounds of Psychic TV and visual images by Hyperdelic Video. Introduction by Nina Graboi, author of *One Foot in the Future*, (her autobiography about her spiritual development using psychedelics.) video - $30. (2 hours)

Understanding Ecstasy: From Psychotherapy to the Rave Culture - audio tapes - Lecture by Bruce Eisner at UC Santa Cruz 2/15/93. Includes one hour lecture and one hour question and answer period, 2 tapes - $16.95.

The Human Situation: Boxed set of 16 audio tapes chronicling a series of lectures Aldous Huxley gave as visiting professor at U.C. Santa Barbara in 1959. He was working on his last novel *Island* when he gave these talks. Some of the titles are: "How Original is Original Sin?"; "Man and Religion"; "Latent Human Potentialities"; "Natural History of Visions", and more. 16 one-hour tapes - $125.

Navigating the Chaotic '90s: Timothy Leary at the Pacific Cultural Center in Santa Cruz, Feb. 28, 1992. An overview of the last two millennium to learn from history how to better surf the waves of change in the chaotic '90s. This is the first time this video has been released. Video, $30 (2 hours)

MushroomPeople

560 Farm Rd. P.O. Box 220 Dept. R
Summertown, TN 39493-0220

(800) 386-4495

**E-mail: mushroom@
 thefarm.org**

Free Catalog

This is the only company I have seen that rents videotapes. *Mushroom Growing Magic* rents for $16/week and deals with the cultivation of wild mushrooms. I've seen this video and it offers good step by step instructions on agar preparation, inoculation of petri dishes,

Continued on next page...

"We never quarrel about religion, because it is a matter which concerns each man and the Great Spirit." - Seneca Chief

production of grain spawn and finally fruiting in aquariums. Other videos for rent - *Sasha Shulgin in Telluride, The Soma Seminar* (where Andrew Weil, Emanuel Salzman and others discuss the varieties of experience following ingestion of *Amanita muscaria*). *A Magical Journey* featuring Terence McKenna, *The Adventure of Self-Discovery* with Stanislav Grof, *From Here to Alternity* with John Lilly, *Consciousness, Conspiracy and Coincidence* with Robert Anton Wilson, and others.

Mystic Fire Direct

P.O. Box 422 Dept. R
New York, NY 10012

800-292-9001

E-mail: mysticfire@echonyc.com
Website: http://www.mysticfire.com

Free Catalog

Has the following audio and video tapes:

Terence McKenna: *History Ends in Green,* 6 tape audio set, 7 hours, $39.95.

This is an excellent tape, recorded in a small group setting with a lot of time devoted to questions and answers. If you've heard a lot of Terence's tapes, the most interesting part of his lectures becomes the Q & A periods because there is always something new to learn from audience questions.

Terence McKenna: *Surfing on Finnegans Wake and Riding Range with Marshall McLuhan,* 2 audio tape set, 2 hours, $18.95

McKenna expounds on James Joyce's classic work about the fall and redemption of humankind and the union of spirit and matter. McKenna on Finnegans Wake: "This is stream of consciousness conceived as a dream. It's as if you had taken the entirety of the last thousand years of human history and dissolved all the boundaries." McKenna on McLuhan: "McLuhan felt that the art, historical and architectural output of Western civilization could be psychoanalyzed . . . could be seen as the tracings of the mass consciousness."

Metamorphosis: A Trialogue with Terence McKenna, Rupert Sheldrake and Ralph Abraham, 88 minute video $29.95.

Terence is joined by Rupert Sheldrake, bi-ologist and originator of the theory of morphogenetic fields and Ralph Abraham, mathematician and exponent of chaos theory. Filmed at Esalen Institute in Big Sur, CA.

Cyberpunk: Featuring Timothy Leary, William Gibson & Jaron Lanier, 60 min video, $29.95.

William Gibson, author of *Neuromancer* and Jaron Lanier, perennial cybertech, join forces with Timothy Leary and explore the world of virtual reality, cyberspace and hackers.

Also available is the excellent *Ring of Fire* series. Also Joseph Campbell's *The Power of Myth* series, and videos by Alan Watts, William Burroughs, Krishnamurti and many others.

Psychedelic Illuminations

P.O. Box 3186 Dept. R
Fullerton, CA 92634

714-733-1252

Free Tape List
$30 for 4 Issues of the magazine

Psychedelic Illuminations magazine sells audio and video tapes of Terence McKenna, Timothy Leary, Jonathan Ott, and Dr. Charles Grob, among others. Most of these tapes were recorded by Ron Piper, editor of the magazine, and you will not find them for sale anywhere else. They also sell audio and video tapes of the Psychedelic Summit held in Santa Cruz in April, 1993. This symposium, held in honor of the 50th anniversary of the discovery of LSD, featured talks by Oscar Janiger, Timothy Leary, Robert Anton Wilson, Steven Gaskin, and Dr. Claudio Naranjo among others. 3 audio tapes - $20, 1 video - $30.

Also available are audio and video tapes of the Psychedelic Symposium held at Chapman University in April 1994. Speakers include Timothy Leary, Dennis McKenna, Peter Stafford, Bruce Eisner, Jonathan Ott, Jim DeKorne, Ralph Metzner, Ram Dass, Rick Doblin and Thomas Pinkson among others. Nine different panel discussions are available.

"In as much as all beings are our kindly parents, it would be a cause of regret to have aversion for and thus disown or abandon any of them." - Tantric precept

Sound Horizons

250 W. 57th St., Suite 1517 Dept. R
New York, NY 10107

(800) 524-8355

Website: http://www.soundhorizons.com

Free Catalog

Sells audio tapes from New York's Open Center

Terence McKenna

Having Archaic and Eating It Too - $9

Light At the End of History - $9

The Edge of Meaning - 2 tapes, $18

Exploring the Hermetic Tradition - 4 tapes, $36

Limits of Art and Edges of Science - $9

Mapping the End of History - 5 tapes, $45

Shamanism - 4 tapes, $36

Global Perspectives and Psychedelic Poetics -
2 tapes, $16.95

True Hallucinations - 2 tapes, $18

Andrew Weil

A Radical View of Addiction -
2 tapes, $18

Stanislov Grof

Death, Dying and Rebirth - 4 tapes, $3
Healing and Non-Ordinary Consciousness -
4 tapes, $3

Sound Photosynthesis

P.O. Box 2111 Dept. R
Mill Valley, CA 94942

(415) 383-6712
(415) 381-3127 - FAX

Website: http://www.photosynthesis.
com/home.html

$2 Catalog
$5 on Mac or DOS Disk

A huge listing of audio and video tapes, certainly the best selection anywhere. They have finally put together a real catalog from all of their loose multi-colored pages of tape lists—a big improvement. Their service can be slow, so be patient; their selection is worth the wait. They have audio and video tapes of most of the participants at the 1991 Bridge Conference "Linking the Past, Present and Future of Psychedelics" at Stanford University. Speakers include McKenna, Leary, Lilly, Peter Stafford, Stephen Gaskin, Francis Huxley, Michael Horowitz, Bruce Eisner, Robert Anton Wilson, Ralph Metzner, Marlene Dobkin de Rios, Charles Tart, Thomas Pinkson, Dennis McKenna and many others. They also have audio and video tapes of the Psychedelic Summit, the exposition held in S.F. in April '93 celebrating the 50th anniversary of Albert Hofmann's discovery of LSD. Many of the same speakers were at this conference. There is also a large selection of audio and video tapes by Terence McKenna, Colin Wilson (one of England's most prolific writers whose interests range from philosophy, the occult, Buddhism, psychedelics, paranormal phenomenon and on...), Stephen Gaskin (seminal figure in the Haight during the, 60's founder of the Farm - the Summertown, Tennessee commune, and author of *Amazing Dope Tales*), Arthur M. Young (founder of the Foundation for the Study of Consciousness, inventor of the Bell helicopter, and author of many books including *The Reflexive Universe* and *The Geometry of Meaning*), Andrew Harvey (author, professor of philosophy and religious studies, and scholar of the work of the mystical Sufi poet Rumi), John Lilly (the King of Ketamine - best known for his years spent developing scientific projects attempting communication with dolphins, he is also the author of *The Center of the Cyclone* and *The Scientist*, among others), Neil Freer (author of *Breaking The Godspell*, he has been influenced by Sumerian scholar Zecharia Sitchin, who proposes we are a genetically engineered species and that science is only now revealing facts that were known thousands of years ago), Robert McDermott (president of the California Institute of Integral Studies, lecturer and author of books on Sri Aurobindo and Rudolph Steiner), plus many more!

"Instead of all this energy and effort directed at the war to end drugs, how about a little attention to drugs which will end war." - Albert Hofmann

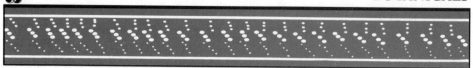

Amazing Nature

P.O. Box 318 Dept. R
6500 AH Nijmegen
The Netherlands

Phone: 01131 24 3780573

E-mail: a_nature@telbyte.nl

Free Catalog (available in English, Dutch, German or Spanish. All prices include shipping).

This is a rather unique business in that they sell such choice items as *Psilocybe cubensis* mushrooms, peyote plants and ayahuasca. These items are legal in The Netherlands, they are illegal in the USA. Amazing Nature will ship anywhere in the world, so you need to find out what the law is regarding these botanicals in your country. If you place an order, you do so at your own risk. Amazing Nature will not give you a refund or credit if your order gets seized by customs. Payment should be made in U.S. dollars (cash) and sent by registered mail, or you can pay cash on delivery for an extra $33.

Dried Mushrooms

Psilocybe cubensis - 2gm/$16.50, 5gm/$33
Psilocybe semilanceata - 1.5gm/$16.50,
    4gm/$33
Copelandia cyanescens - 1gm/$16.50,
    2.5gm/$33

Copelandia is the most potent of these three mushrooms. Mushrooms are shipped whole unless requested otherwise.

Sporeprints

Psilocybe cubensis - $33
Psilocybe cyanescens - $40

Home Grow Set - "Finest quality mycelium. Everything you need to harvest between 250-400 gm *P. cubensis* mushrooms" - $115.50

B-Wax - 100ml (about 2 cup) of honey containing 3gm dried *P. cubensis* - $18.15

Ayahuasca - You get a Syrian rue extract (made from 3gm Syrian rue) and a *Psychotria viridis* extract (made from 30gm of dried leaves). This is sufficient for one bio-assay. Instructions included - $40

Yopo - This is a traditional snuff made from the seeds of *Anadenanthera peregrina*, which has a long history of use by the Indian tribes of South America. *Anadenanthera* seeds contain DMT, 5-MeO-DMT, and 5-OH-DMT (bufotenine). Snuff made from these seeds is quite painful when snorted and not particularly visionary. I would not recommend trying this unless you have a high tolerance for pain.

Peyote (*Lophophora williamsii*) - These are rooted cacti, not the cut buttons. They are 4-6 years old and approx. 2" in diameter at the crown - $31.35/cacti.

San Pedro (*T. pachanoi*) - These are 3-5" unrooted cuttings, approx. 2" in diameter. U.S. residents would do much better ordering from a domestic source where you will get much more for you money - $23/cacti.

Trichocereus Bridgesii - same size and price as San Pedro.

Marijuana seeds - "Ten powerful selected Skunk seeds from Holland for indoor and outdoor growing. Produces large plants (up to 9 ft.) with lots of big buds."

Amazing Mint - A candy made of marijuana and peppermint leaves. - $16.50.

Aztekakti

P.O. Box 26126 Dept. R
11306 Gateway East
El Paso, TX 79927

(915) 858-1130

$1 Catalog

Sells seeds only of cacti and succulents. They have seeds of 17 *Trichocereus* species. They do not have seeds of *T. pachanoi* or *T. peruvianus*, but a number of the other *Trichocereus* species they carry are of ethnopharmacological interest. You get 1000 seeds for $2.50.

"Penalties against the possession of a drug should not be more damaging to the individual than the use of the drug itself." - Jimmy Carter

Basement Shaman

P.O. Box 1255 Dept. R
Elgin, IL 60121

E-mail: bshaman@interaccess.com

$2 Catalog

Their catalog has been greatly expanded with many more botanical products and a small but good selection of books (see "Book Catalogs"). This is the best looking ethnobotanical catalog on the market. They give thorough, detailed descriptions of their botanical products, stating the origin and history of use of each plant. They also offer mycological services, (see "Spore Germination"). A few choice Terence McKenna tapes are offered as well (see "Audio and Video Tapes"). Highly recommended.

Artimisia absinthium
Dried foliage - 8 oz/$9, 1lb/$16
Arundo donax - live plant - inquire for price
Banisteriopsis caapi - live plant-$35
Desmanthus illinoensis
Rootstock - 8oz/$30, 1lb/$50
Heimia salicifolia (live plant) - $12
Justicia pectoralis - live plant-inquire for price
Papaver somniferum
10 gm/$22, 25 gm/$38
Peganum harmala
1 oz/$10, 8 oz/$36
Seed Resin Extract (1 gm resin=3 gm seed)
10 gm/$15, 20 gm/$27
Phalaris arundinacea
"Turkey Red strain" live plant - $25
Phalaris aquatica
Varieties: Australian, Sirosa, Unita or AQ1
5 plugs/$25, 10 plugs/$45, 25 plugs/$85
AQ1 - 5 plugs/$30, 10 plugs/$53
Piper betel - live plant - inquire for price
Salvia divinorum -
live plant - $35
"Palatable" clone - $45
Dried leaves - 10 gm/$28, 25 gm/$60
Theobroma cacao -
live plant - $24/1yr old treelet
Trichocereus pachanoi
10"-16" cuttings with tips - $30

8"-12" rooted cuttings - $22
8"-12" unrooted cuttings - $15
Calea zacatechichi - 2 oz dried foliage - $24
Banisteriopsis caapi
Dried vine sections - 3 oz/$32, 8 oz/$81,
Kava Kava
Chopped dry roots - 8 oz/$18, 1 lb/$34
Psychotria viridis
live plant - $65 - limited quantity - send SASE or e-mail before ordering. -
dried leaves 25 gm/$28, 50 gm/$53, 100 gm/$100
Huambisa Chacruna strain 25gm/$32, 50gm/$58, 100gm/$105

Bert Marco Schuldes

Hauptstrasse 70 Dept. R
99759 Rehungen
Germany

**E-mail:mail-order@dreamspace.o
mp-paderborn.de**

$1 information sheet

Bert sells an alcohol based extract of *Salvia divinorum* for use as an experimental natural dye. It will stain damn near anything an intense green color. Bert grows the plants himself without the use of pesticides or fungicides, and fertilizes them with homemade compost. The info. sheet warns that the extract must not be used internally or altered states of mind will result. He includes a summary of his experiences ingesting the dye to discourage anyone from trying this. The info. sheet is well worth ordering even if you have no need for a green dye.

5ml bottle (2 units) - $15 + $4 S&H

10ml bottle (4 units) - $25 + $7 S&H

The following *Cannabis* seeds are also available. Seeds will be shipped anywhere, but U.S. customers be aware it is illegal to import *Cannabis* seeds into this country. All prices given are in German Deutschemarks.

Continued on next page...

Positronics
Per pack of 5 seeds DM 15

   Afghani

   Aurora Borealis (Northern Lights)

   Skunk Special

   Holland's Hoop

Original Skunkman
Per pack of 5 seeds DM 15

   Afghani #1

   The Original Skunk #1

   Early Girl

   Durban Poison x Skunk #1

Dutch Passion
Prices per 10 seeds, prices in DM

Oasis (Northern Lights)	60
Thai	70
Afghani #1	40
Skunk #1	35
Durban Poison	50
Indoor Mix	3
Outdoor Mix	25

Sensi Seeds
Prices per 15 seeds in DM

Shiva Shanti	60
Jack Herer (High Times Cup Winner May 1995)	275
Northern Lights	200
Hawaiian Indica	125
Big Bud	160
Afghani	90
Hindu Kush	100
Super Skunk	80
Early Pearl	100
Durban	100

Payment with postal money order or U.S. dollars (cash). If sending cash use registered mail. Wholesale inquiries welcome. S & H DM 5. Additional information on shipping available on request.

BM
217 W. Moneta Dept. R
Bakersfield, CA 93308

No Catalog

This small business offers the following items:

Trichocereus pachanoi seeds
   $3/50 seeds, $5/100 seeds

Trichocereus peruvianus seeds
   $3/50 seeds, $5/100 seeds

L. williamsii growing instructions - $5

Extract LSA (lysergic acid amides) from morning glory or baby Hawaiian woodrose seeds instructions - $5

Shipping is free with SASE

Companion Plants
7247 N. Coolville Ridge Rd. Dept. R
Athens, OH 45701

(614) 592-4643

Website:http://www.frognet.
  net companion_plants/

$3 Catalog

Some of their listings include:

baby Hawaiian woodrose plant - $7, seed pkt. - $2

Datura plant - various species - $4, seed pkt. - $2

Heimia salicifolia plant - $5, seed pkt. - $2

Rivea corymbosa plant - $10

Salvia divinorum plant - $25

Peganum harmala plant - $6, seed pkt. - $2

Banisteriopsis caapi plant - $80

G. Köhres
Wingerstrabe 33 Dept. R
D-64387 Erzhausen/Darmstadt
Germany

$2 Catalog

   Lophophora williamsii seeds and many species of *Trichocereus* are available from this company. Not knowing what their prices were, I sent them $20 and received 180 *L. williamsii* seeds (11¢ /each). This was 2 years ago, but even if their prices have gone up, this is the least expensive source you will find for these seeds.

"There is no such thing as 'my' consciousness; there is just consciousness acting as a continuity that is moving across all forms of evolution, from mineral to man." - pir vilayat inayat khan

Gnostic Garden

P.O. Box 1 ED Dept. R
Newcastle Upon Tyne
NE99 1ED U.K.

Catalog $3 - overseas
$2 - Europe
£1 - U.K.

This is a relatively new company that carries over 80 different species of seeds and plants. A good looking catalog with a great selection that is focused on ethnobotanicals. Of special interest is their listing of *Lophophora williamsii* (peyote seeds). Payment can be made in International Money Order made payable to D. Gibson - not Gnostic Garden. Payment can also be made in foreign currency (cash) by sending in your order without payment - state the currency you wish to pay in - and you will be sent an invoice with amount owed. Live plants and cacti cannot be sent overseas. They are willing to do trades if you have seeds or live specimens of anything interesting that is not listed in their catalog.

A partial list of their botanicals include:
Wormwood - £1.50/seed pkt.
Atropa belladonna - £2/seed pkt.
Calea zacatechichi- £10/live plant
Ipomoea violacea
   Heavenly Blue - seed pkt - £1. 5/1oz
   Flying Saucers - pkt - £2
   Pearly Gates - pkt-£2
Lophophora williamsii seed - £4.50
Papaver somniferum (opium poppy) - £1.30
Peganum harmala (Syrian rue)
   viable seed pkt - £2
   1 oz non-viable seed - £5
Phalaris aquatica - AQ1 strain - £2.50
Trichocereus pachanoi -seeds- £2.50
Trichocereus peruvianus -seeds- £2.50
Psychotria virides - £5/5seeds
Salvia divinorum - £15/live plant

Horus Botanicals

HCR 82 Box 29 Dept. R
Salem, AR 72576

$3 Catalog

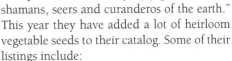

Offers "Herbs, seeds, and plants utilized by shamans, seers and curanderos of the earth." This year they have added a lot of heirloom vegetable seeds to their catalog. Some of their listings include:

Banisteriopsis caapi vine - $45
Brugmansia rooted cutting - $12
Brugmansia, various species - $12/plant
Brunfelsia various species - $15
Yohimbe bark $6.25 / oz
Datura, various species - $3/seed pkt
Desmanthus illinoensis seed pkt - $2
Heimia salicifolia dried leaves $10/oz, seeds-$3
Kava Kava
Whole root - $4.25/oz, $33.70/lb
Powdered root - $4.29/oz, $34.30/lb
Psychotria vridis - $25/plant
Morning Glory
   Flying Saucers - $3/seed pkt.
   Heavenly Blue - $2/seed pkt.
   Pearly Gates - $2/seed pkt.
   Blue Star - $3/5 seeds
Papaver somniferum seed pkt. -$4
Peganum harmala seed pkt. - $3
Salvia divinorum plant - $25
Trichocereus pachanoi seed pkt. - $4
Many more listings in large catalog.

Ho Ti Products

P.O. Box 679 Dept. R
Honaunau, HI 96726

E-mail: hoti@ilhawaii.net
Website: http://www.ilhawaii.net:80/~hoti/

Ho Ti sells live plants only and has great prices on *Salvia divinorum*.

Live Plant List

Banisteriopsis caapi - $35
Catha edulis (khat) - $24
Datura (triple cream, annual) $9
Datura candida (white tree) - $18

Continued on next page..

"As the caterpillar chooses the fairest leaves to lay eggs on, so the priest lays his curse on the fairest joys." - William Blake

29

Datura inoxia (white annual) - $14

Datura metel (double purple annual) - $9

Datura versicolor (orange tree) - $15

baby Hawaiian woodrose - $14

Justicia pectoralis - $20

Kava Kava - $15

Black Kava - $18

Kukui nut tree, *Aleurites molucanna* - $10

Mamaki, *Pipturus albidus* - $14

Mayan mint - $12

Salvia divinorum - $20

Salvia divinorum (palatable clone) - $25

Send check or money order, add 4.2% tax and $5 S&H (cannot ship to: CA, LA, TX)

JLF

P.O. Box 184 Dept. R
Elizabethtown, IN 47232

812-379-2508

$2 Catalog

This company sells "Natural, uniquely poisonous products." They specialize in *Amanita muscaria* mushrooms.

Amanita muscaria - "Red Fly Agaric"

Grade A 30 gm - $60

Grade B 30 gm - $50

Grade B 1 lb - $500

Grade C 30 gm - $35

Grade D 30 gm - $33

Resin Extract - 20 gm - $42
(from yellow fly agaric)

Some other offerings:

Banisteriopsis caapi
vine - $20/60gm
B caapi foliage - $20/90 gm

Yohimbe bark - $15/60 gm

Datura stramonium "Jimson weed"
Foliage - 60 gm/$12
Seeds - 60 gm/$17
Roots - 60 gm/$14

Desmanthus illinoensis
Roots - 60 gm/$10
Seeds - 60gm/$10

Morning Glory seeds

various kinds & prices

Papaver somniferum - 5gm/$10

Peganum harmala "Syrian rue"
Seeds - 30 gm/$8, 120gm/$20
Seed resin extract - 20 gm/$25

Phalaris arundinacea
Foliage - 120 gm/$15, 1 lb/$40
Seeds - 90 gm/$13, 270 gm/$30

Piper methysticum "Kava Kava"
Roots - 120 gm/$15
Root resin extract - 15 gm/$25

Psychotria viridis
30gm (dried leaves) - $30

Salvia divinorum foliage
14gm/$35, 30 gm/$70

Trichocereus pachanoi "San Pedro"
live plant $31.50

Cactus slices - 50 gm equals 18" of fresh cactus $18, 1lb/$125

Kava Kauai

6817 Kahuna Rd. Dept. R
Kapaa, HI 96746

(800) 626-0883

E-mail: photon@hawaiian.net

Free Catalog

This company sells the best Kava I have ever tried. It is from Fiji and grown on the island of Vanua Levu, which is known for its potent strains of Kava. It is Waka grade, the top grade made entirely from the lateral roots which have the highest concentration of the kavalactones - the active ingredient. The first thing I noticed about this Kava was its smell - more intense and pungent than any I have smelled before. Kava produces a mild but very pleasurable effect, it relaxes the body but stimulates the mind and creates a sociable, easy going mood. One serving is a heaping 1/4 cup and there are 12 servings per pound.

Kava Kauai also sells dried *Salvia divinorum* leaves that are as good as any I have had. Their *Salvia* plants are organically grown and the leaves are air dried They are also the only company that sells fresh *Salvia* leaves. You must order these by express mail, which costs $15, because the leaves do not last long once they

"Hope is effort, not wish; effort to make it so; not a wish that it may be so." -
G. Gurdjieff

have been picked. If you have been wanting to try chewing the leaves fresh, (which is the best method in my opinion), and don't want to bother with growing the plant, now you can.

Their service is quick and they were very helpful with my questions. If you are in the market for Kava or *Salvia divinorum*, this is the source I recommend.

Ground Kava root
$16/8 oz, $28/lb
Add $3.50 S&H

Salvia divinorum, dried leaves
$20/7gm, $40/14gm, $75/oz
Add $2.50 S&H

Salvia divinorum,, fresh leaves
$25/50 gm. (about 24 large leaves) + $15 express shipping

Banisteriopsis caapi - live plant $40

Bee Mellow - Mixture of Kava & honey
$6/2oz, $10/4oz

Buzz Honey - mixture of honey, guarana, kava, bee pollen & ginkgo extract
$6/2oz, $10/4oz

Double Root Kava Extract (concentrated liquid extract of Kava combined with Chinese licorice root.) $10/1oz. dropper bottle

Psychotria viridis - live plant $75
Seeds - $10/25 seeds

Inquire for shipping costs on live plants.

Kykeon
P.O. Box 1690 Dept. R
46080 Valencia
Spain

Free Price List

This is a new company, and although I have never placed an order with them, I have been in contact with them and they seem reputable. None of Kykeon's products are intended for internal consumption. All product information is given for historical value only.

Psychotria viridis leaves - $25/30gm.
Yohimbe bark - $15/4oz., $30/lb.

Yohimbe HCL
$30/gm, $100/5gm, $300/25gm

Main alkaloid in *Yohimbe* bark. It is a stimulant and mild perceptual alterant. Has sexual stimulating properties as well.

Payment should be in U.S. dollars (cash) sent registered mail. Kykeon has other products such as Procaine, L-Tryptophan, and PPA.

LER

P.O. Box 1676 Dept. R
Coconut Grove, FL 33233
(305) 649-9997
E-mail: heruka@shadow.net
Website: http://www.shadow.net/~heruka

$3 Catalog

Legendary Ethnobotanical Resources sells plants, seeds, herbs, teas, books, essential oils, homeopathic remedies, smoking blends and more. Their website lists a vastly expanded selection of botanicals-do they really keep all of these in stock? Order and find out. I do recommend this company. Some of their listings are:

Anadenanthera colubrina plant - $65

Artemisia - wormwood plant - $3.50

Arundo donax plant - $20

Banisteriopsis caapi
5' dried vine sections - $30
Live plant - $45, $100/7 plants
Tincture - $18/oz

Brugmansia - many species available

Catha edulis (khat) plant - $25

Datura stramonium seeds - $4/pkt., $25/1 oz

Desmanthus illinoensis plant- $13, seeds - $4/pkt., $15/7gm

Heimia salicifolia plant - $12, seeds - $5

Ipomoea seed - various species/prices

Kava Kava - Plant $25, powdered root $15.90/ 2 oz, $24.29/4 oz, $45.25/lb

Peganum harmala - $5/seed pkt, $15/oz

Phalaris arundinacea dried grass - $15/oz, $45/4 oz

Phalaris arundinacea seed - $2/pkt., $10/oz, $25/4 oz

P. cubensis spore print $15

Continued on next page...

"There was, from the very beginning, no need for a struggle between the finite and the infinite. The peace we are seeking so eagerly has been there all the time." - D.T. Suzuki

Salvia divinorum plant 'Palatable clone'- $48
  Dried leaves - $30/7gm, $55/14gm,
  $95/oz, $295/100gm
Trichocereus pachanoi, rooted - $22
Trichocereus pachanoi, unrooted
  $17/ft., $70/5', $120/10'
T. pachanoi seeds - $5/100
T. peruvianus unrooted - $35/ft.
Yohimbe bark - $7/2oz, $11/4oz, $20/8oz

Magic
395 Oak Creek, Suite 508 Dept. R
Wheeling, IL 60090

$1 Catalog

Sells live plants and
dried leaves of
Salvia divinorum.

Salvia divinorum live plant -
  $35/3" - 4" rooted cutting
  $45/7" - 8" rooted cutting
Dried leaves - $35/14 gm.

The Salvia Report - covers growing, preparation and use of this unique plant. - $5 (This
report is free if your order is over $50.)

Plants are only shipped by next day air - add
$15 for shipping. See Magic's other listing in
the Miscellaneous section.

Native Habitat
P.O. Box 4023 Dept. R
Vero Beach, FL 32964

$1 Catalog ($2 foreign)

Some of their offerings:
Banisteriopsis caapi
  $20/plant, $30/1lb fresh stems
Kava Kava - $15/plant
Piper betel
  $10/plant, $7/1lb fresh leaf,
  $10/Indian Betel Nut Chew

They also have a large selection of *Brugmansia*
and *Datura* plants.

New Mexico Cactus Research
P.O. Box 787 Dept. R
Belen, NM 87002

(505) 864-4027

$1 Catalog

Sells seeds and cuttings of cacti and succulents. If you want to get *Trichocereus* cuttings,
they have the best selection. Some offerings:
T. pachanoi stock:
  Unrooted tip cuts, various lengths,
  2.5" dia. - $1.00/in
  Without tips - 2.5" dia. - $1.00/in.

Call for exact price & shipping cost

Osaanyin Herb Cooperative
104 Main St. Dept. R
Montpelier, VT 05602

(802) 223-0888

$1 Catalog

This is a small collec-
tively owned and operated
business. They offer over
400 botanicals in bulk as
well as tinctures, oils, salves, Chinese herbal
patent formulas and herbal books. Many of
their products are organically grown or wild-
crafted. A conscientious company that de-
serves your support. Some of their offerings:

Kava Kava - $2.75/oz
Yohimbe root bark - $9/oz
Banisteriopsis caapi - $10/10" vine section
Desmanthus illinoensis Root - Inquire
baby Hawaiian woodrose seeds
  $2.50/10, $20/100
Peganum harmala seeds - $10/oz

"If you want peace of mind, do not find fault with others." - Sarada devi

P.J.T. Botanics

P.O. Box 49 Dept. R
Bridgewater, MA 02324

$3 Catalog

A good selection of plants and seeds. They have the lowest ounce prices on *Psychotria viridis* leaves of any company. A few of their offerings:

Banisteriopsis caapi
$20/plant, $75/1oz. Dried vine sections (plants available only in June-August)

Corynanthe yohimbe - $6/1oz. dried bark

Datura stramonium - $2/25 seeds

Desmanthus illinoensis - $4/100 seeds

baby Hawaiian woodrose seeds
$3/10 seeds, $15/100, $30/1oz.

Ipomoea violacea (morning glory)
Flying Saucers - $4/5 seed
Heavenly Blue - $10/1oz.
Pearly Gates - $10/1oz.
Scarlet O'hara - $12/1oz.

Mimosa hostilis - $5/seed pkt.

Papaver somniferum - $10/10,000 seeds

Peganum harmala - $15/1oz. viable seeds
$8/1oz. non-viable seeds

Kava Kava - $4/1oz. roots

Psychotria viridis - $25/1oz. dried leaves

Salvia divinorum - $35/plant
(available only in June-August)

Trichocereus pachanoi - $20/12" rooted cutting,
$4.50/100 seeds

Trichocereus peruvianus - $55/6" rooted cutting,
$5.50/100 seeds

Redwood City Seed Co.

P.O. Box 361 Dept. R
Redwood City, CA 94064

415-325-SEED

Website: http://www.
batnet.com/rwc-seed/

$1 Catalog

Sells mostly vegetable seeds but has a small section entitled "Specialty Plants" which include the following (call or check Website for current prices):

Catha edulis (khat)

Datura stramonium

Datura meteloides

Heimia salicifolia seed pkt.

Morning Glory - Heavenly Blue or
Pearly Gates

Salvia divinorum plant

Calea zacatechichi

Peganum harmala

baby Hawaiian woodrose

Smart Botanics

Postbus 158 Dept. R
2800 AD Gouda
The Netherlands

Website: http://WWW.xs4all.nl-psee/
indexeng.html

This company offers dried *Psilocybe* mushrooms to their customers in the Netherlands - but does not ship them overseas. They offer the following items for export:

P. cubensis sporeprint - $19

Smart Syringe (contains *P. cubensis* spores in water) - $8

baby Hawaiian woodrose seeds - $6/10 seeds
add $3 S&H to any of the above items.

For sale within the Netherlands are the following:

P. cubensis mushrooms - 2.5 gm dried - $10.50

P. semilanceata - 1 gm dried - $17

Copelandia cyanescens - .8 gm dried - $17

Tech Enterprises

180 Hidden Lakes, Suite H-5 Dept. R
Macon, GA 31204

800-293-7648

$1 catalog

Kava kava - $16/4oz., $37/lb.

Corynanthe yohimbe - $16/4oz., $36/lb.

Trichocereus pachanoi -
$40/ 2½ x 15" cutting
Seeds - $40/100, $100/500

Timberwolf Gardens

P.O. Box 264 Dept. R
Fords, NJ 08863

Free Price List w/SASE

A small selection of botanicals including:

San Pedro - 8-10" stock - $30

Peganum harmala seeds - $15/oz, $100/lb

Banisteriopsis caapi vine sections - $55/5'

Kava Kava powdered root: $20/100 capsules, $5/oz, $30/lb

Yohimbe bark - $11/oz, $35/4 oz,

Yohimbe bark concentrate - $25/oz

Amanita muscaria mushrooms - $50/30 gm, $75/30 gm resin extract

baby Hawaiian woodrose - $5/10 seeds, $30/100 seeds

large Hawaiian woodrose - $20/oz, $150/lb

Morning Glory Seeds
Heavenly Blue - $10/oz, $30/4 oz
Pearly Gates - $18/oz, $54/4 oz

Weeds

P.O. Box 161061 Dept. R
Austin, TX 78716

Free Catalog

This business sells weeds because ". . . they are easy to care for . . . and in the proper environment will become intensely aggressive and invasive. . ."

Some of their offerings are:

Arundo donax (Giant Reed) - $15/live rhizome

Desmanthus illinoensis - $2/seed pkt.

Heimia salicifolia - $25/plant, $10/rooted cutting, $2/seeds

Banisteriopsis caapi - $35/plant

They also sell a number of reports which it appears they write themselves. Some of them are:

Cultivation of Desmanthus for Root Bark Production - 5 pp. - $2

Cultivation of Cactus - 19 pp. - $5

Pharmacognosis and Religious Experience Vol. I - 350 pp. - $15

Thoughts on Hallucinogens and the Law 13 pp. - $2

The Peyote Crisis and Some Suggestions 7 pp. - $2

Wildflowers of Heaven

P.O. Box 1989 Dept. R
Ranchos de Taos, NM 87557

$2 Catalog
$5 Catalog & 1 year of new product updates   Add 25% of order for shipping under $25 Free shipping on orders over $25.

I went through a protracted dispute with this company regarding the authenticity of the *Trichocereus peruvianus* cactus they are selling. I ordered 2 cuttings and had some very knowledgeable people inspect them and there was unanimous agreement that they were not *T. peruvianus*. Wildflowers acquiesced and changed the name to *T. mescalito*, then changed it to *T. peru*, but they still state in their catalog "It's our opinion that anyone wanting a *T. peruvianus* plant would be just as happy with these - we believe them to be genuine *T. peruvianus*, but to not offend anyone, we've given them an alias to indicate it's only our opinion." Well, it is my opinion you will not be "just as happy" with these grossly overpriced mystery cacti. Order their *T. pachanoi* instead, or order *T. peruvianus* from another company. If you have been wanting to buy a *T. peruvianus*, educate yourself as to what it looks like - I have a feeling this is not the only company selling a mysterious *Trichocereus* hybrid as genuine *T. peruvianus*.

Some of their botanicals:

Morning Glory - Heavenly Blue - $2/50, $5/300, $9/oz, $30/4oz, $70/lb

baby Hawaiian woodrose seeds - $7.50/10, $25/50, $45/100

Trichocereus pachanoi cactus

Unrooted cuttings: 8"x2" - $15, 6"x3" - $18, 12"x32" - $36,
No rooted stock available

Trichocereus peruvianus seeds $4/50 seeds, $6/100, $20/500

Trichocereus pachanoi seeds - $3.50/50

seeds, $5/100, $18/500

Trichocereus bridgesii seeds -same % magic
as San Pedro, $3.50/50 seeds, $5/100 seeds

Peganum harmala seed - $8/oz, $22/3oz

Guarana Extract (powdered form)
$9/oz, $20/3.5oz

"Growing Cacti from Seed" Report - $5, In-
cludes instructions for *Lophophora*,
Trichocereus and others.

"Cactus Grafting" Report - $5, Instructions for
increasing cactus growth by grafting slow
growing species (such as *Lophophora*)
onto fast growing species (*Trichocereus*).

"Growing Cacti from Cuttings" Report - $5
All three reports - $10

Peganum harmala plants
3 yr old - $12.50 ea, 3 for $30

*"By nature's kindly disposition, most questions which it is beyond a person's power to answer
do not occur to them at all." - Santayana*

35

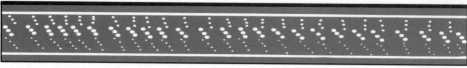

The prices that most botanical companies charge for Syrian rue are outrageous and unjustified. If you live in a large city, you can find Syrian rue in a Middle Eastern grocery store for as little as $14/lb - that's .88/oz! It will be called esphand or esfand

Basement Shaman

P.O. Box 1255 Dept. R
Elgin, IL 60121
E-mail: bshaman@
   interaccess.com

$2 Catalog

Peganum harmala seeds
   $10/oz
   $36/8 oz
Seed resin extract (3 gm seed=1 gm resin)
   $15/10 gm, $27/20 gm
baby Hawaiian woodrose
   $16/1/2 oz
   $28/oz
Papaver somniferum
   $22/10 gm, $38/25 gm

Blue Ridge Garden

P.O. Box 52 Dept. R
Mint Spring, VA 24463

No Catalog
Free Shipping

large Hawaiian woodrose seeds
   1 oz - $1
   4 oz - $35
Morning Glory seeds
   1 oz - $10
   4 oz - $35
Imported Poppy
   10,000 - $10
   4 oz - $50
   1 lb - $150

Borealis

21150 Hawthorne Blvd #106-119 Dept. R
Torrance, CA 90503

Peganum harmala seeds
   $5/oz, $10/3 oz, $20/7 oz

JLF

P.O. Box 184 Dept. R
Elizabethtown, IN 47232
812-379-2508

$2 Catalog

Morning Glory seeds - 60 gm/$17,
   250 gm/$60, 1lb/$100

Peganum harmala seeds, 30 gm/$10
   Seed Resin Extract - 20 gm/$25

baby Hawaiian woodrose - 30gm/$20

LER

P.O. Box 1676Dept. R
Coconut Grove, FL 33233
(305) 649-9997
E-mail: heruka@shadow.net
Website: http://www.shadow.
   net/~heruka

$2 Catalog

baby Hawaiian woodrose
   50 seeds $12
   100 seeds $20
   500 seeds $85
   Living plant $14

Morning Glory seeds
   Heavenly Blue $15/oz, $115/lb
   Pearly Gates - $20/oz, $125/lb
   Blue Star (rare) - $1 per seed

Osaanyin Herb Cooperative

104 Main St. Dept. R
Montpelier, VT 05602
802-223-0888

$1 Catalog

Peganum harmala seeds - $10/oz

baby Hawaiian woodrose seeds
   $2.50/10, $20/100

Pacific Exotic Spora
P.O. Box 1161 Dept. R
Honolulu, HI 96828

$2 Catalog

large Hawaiian woodrose

$9/1/2oz
$17/1oz
$52/4oz

P.J.T. Botanicals
P.O. Box 49 Dept. R
Birdgewater, MA 02324

$3 Catalog

baby Hawaiian woodrose - $3/10 seeds, $15/100, $30/oz.

Morning Glory

Flying Saucers - $4/5 seeds
Heavenly Blue - $10/oz.
Pearly Gates - $10/oz.
Scarlet O'hara - $12/oz.

Peganum harmala - $15/oz. viable seeds, $8/oz. non-viable seeds

Seed Tech
180 Hidden Lakes, Suite H5, Dept. R
Macon, GA 31204

800-293-7648

baby Hawaiian woodrose
$35/oz
$120/4oz
$350/lb

large Hawaiian woodrose
$25/2oz
$40/4oz
$100/lb

Morning Glory
Heavenly Blue
$25/2oz
$40/oz
$100/lb

Pearly Gates
$35/2oz
$60/4oz
$100/8oz
$150/lb

Peganum harmala
$25/2oz
$40/4oz
$60/8oz
$100/lb

Poppy Seeds (imported)
$15/oz
$25/2oz
$40/4oz

T.A.E.
1935 S. Plum Grove Rd. Dept. R
Suite #348
Palatine, IL 60067

800-870-7333

Free Price List
Prices Include Shipping

large Hawaiian woodrose seeds
$20/oz
$35/2oz
$30/4oz
$95/lb

Timberwolf Gardens
P.O. Box 264 Dept. R
Fords, NJ 08863

Free Price List w/SASE

Baby Hawaiian woodrose
$5/10 seeds, $30/100 seeds

large Hawaiian woodrose
$20/oz, $150/lb

Morning Glory seeds
Heavenly Blue - $10/oz, $30/4 oz
Pearly Gates - $18/oz, $54/4 oz

Peganum harmala seeds - $15/oz, $100/lb

"If you can't stand solitude perhaps you bore others too." - anon.

Wildflowers of Heaven
P.O. Box 1989 Dept. R
Ranchos de Taos, NM 87577

$2 Catalog
$5 Catalog & one year of
  new product updates

Add 25% of order total for shipping
Free shipping on orders over $25

Morning Glory seeds
Heavenly Blue

  $2/50 seeds
  $5.50/10gm
  $12/oz
  $30/3oz
  $90/lb

Baby Hawaiian woodrose seeds

  $7.50/10
  $25/50
  $45/100

Peganum harmala seeds

  $2/50
  $8/oz
  $22/3oz

"A man wrapped up in himself makes a small package." - anon.

The Entheogen Law Reporter

P.O. Box 73481 Dept. R
Davis, CA 95617-3481

Website: http://www.
cyberverse.com/
~martins/TELR/

$25 for 1yr (4 issues)
Back Issues - $5 each

The Complete Entheogen Law Reporter (issues 1-10 of *TELR*) $24.95 + $3.50 S&H app. 100 pp.

Make check payable to: Richard Glen Boire

This is an excellent newsletter written by Richard Glen Boire, an attorney who specializes in appellate drug cases. This newsletter is not associated with *The Entheogen Review* and covers only the legal aspect of entheogens, no growing techniques, extraction procedures or dose information here. Its purpose is to "provide the latest information and commentary on the intersection of entheogenic substances and the law." *The Entheogen Law Reporter* is well written and does not contain a lot of confusing legal terminology - highly recommended. Eleven issues have been published so far. The highlights include: **Issue #1 (Winter '93)** - An Up To Date Listing of Schedule 1 Hallucinogens; Entheogens Outlawed in 1993; Selected 1993 Court Cases Concerning Entheogens. **Issue #2 (Spring '94) -** Federal Mushroom Conviction Upheld; State by State Peyote exemptions; 2C-B Update; Editorial - Criminalizing Nature and Knowledge. **Issue #3 (Summer '94) -** Magic Mushrooms and the Law; Spore Seller Raided; Religious Freedom Restoration Act Asserted in Peyote Case; *Bufo alvarius* Update; Mail Order Federal Paraphernalia Act. **Issue #4 (Fall '94)** - Practical Legal Aspects For Individuals Using Entheogens, Founder Of Marijuana Using Church Arrested; Recent LSD Carrier Weight Cases; Mail Search Update. **Issue #5 (Winter '94) -** The Jurisprudence of Peyote in the U.S.; Ayahuasca Question; Ketamine Notes; Recent Cases. **Issue #6 (Spring '95) -** Recent Cases Significantly Reducing Federal LSD Sentences; Ketamine Related Arrests; International Mail Search Case; LSD Sentence Entrapment; Indiana Case: Psilocybin Versus *Psilocybe* Mushroom. **Issue #7 (Summer '95) -** Opium - Using Hmong Shaman Wins Reprieve; The Legal Status of *Catha edulis* (khat); Plant Growing Equipment as Illegal Drug Paraphernalia?; AIRFA Protects Peyote Use on Probation; Final Rule with Respect to 2C-B; The Silencing of Opposing Viewpoints; Prior Ingestion of LSD Does Not Defeat Possession Conviction. **Issue #8 (Fall '95) -** Indiana Court Affirms Man's *Psilocybe* Mushroom Conviction; Federal Anti-Drug Laws May Violate the Commerce Clause; LSD-Possession Conviction Upheld Based on Past Possession; Landmark Cases in Entheogen Law - The Neo-American Church Case; DEA Rejects Church's Request for Equal Access to Sacramental Peyote. **Issue #9 (Winter '95) -** Chicago Police Seize Artwork; Entheogens Around the World; Spore prints; Ordering from Exotic Plant Companies; Controlled Substance Analogues; Manufacturing Nitrous Oxide; Supreme Court Hears LSD Case. **Issue #10 (Spring '96) -** Ninth Circuit Holds RFRA Applies in Entheogen Cases; Supreme Court Decides LSD Case; Government Returns Peyote and Drops Charges Against AZ Couple; Shulgin Legal Fund Announced; Minor's Conviction for Possessing "Fake" LSD Upheld; Florida Psilocybe Case Prevents Conviction; CSP Presents "Code of Ethics for Spiritual Guides" **Issue #11 - (Summer '96) -** Author of *Opium for the Masses* Arrested for Possessing Poppies; Federal Court Addresses Meaning of "Religion" Under RFRA; Thoughts on Jury Nullification in Entheogen Cases; Entheogen-related Arrests in the News; On the Legality of *Cannabis*, Peyote and Poppy Seeds, Conferences. Announcement: The Lyceum.

"There is no need to run outside for better seeing. . . Rather, abide at the center of your being; for the more you leave it, the less you learn. Search your heart and see - the way to do is to be." - Lao-Tzu

39

The Entheogen Review

P.O. Box 800 Dept. R
El Rito, NM 87530

$20 for 1 yr. - 4 issues
Back Issues $5 each - (12/92 through 6/96)
First year of publication available as bound
74 page book $20 (9/92, 12/92, 3/93, 6/93)

This is an excellent, one-of-a-kind publication. Subscribers write in about their own experiences with psychotropic plants. They share specific and detailed information about cultivation, preparation, extraction and ritual usage. If you have a question or an experience you want to share, you can write in and possibly get your letter printed. There is so much misinformation, speculation, myth and innuendo surrounding entheogens and their use, this newsletter provides a much needed forum for sharing techniques of proper plant use. They have devoted quite a bit of space to ayahuasca analogues, plant sources of DMT, MAO inhibitors and *Salvia divinorum*. You'll also find useful info. on morning glory seeds, San Pedro preparation, *Amanita muscaria* and much more. Editor Jim DeKorne (author of *Psychedelic Shamanism*) is a knowledgeable, level headed arbiter amidst the maelstrom of information out there. I cannot recommend this publication highly enough, it is my favorite read.

Eleusis

(Order From)
Mind Books
321 S. Main St. #543 Dept. R
Sebastopol, CA 95472

(800) 829-8127

Free Catalog

Issues 1-3 $8.95/ea + $4 S&H

Eleusis is the publication of the Italian Society for the Study of the States of Consciousness. The editor is Giorgio Samorini, the researcher who has studied the *Phalaris* genus extensively and published reports on its use in pharmahuasca.

Some articles in each issue of *Eleusis* are in Italian and some are in English. There have been 3 issues released so far. The articles mentioned below are all in English.

Issue #1: Introduction by Albert Hofmann; Giorgio Samorini on the Indigenous Mushrooms of Africa's Ivory Coast; James Calloway on Ayahuasca.

Issue #2: James Calloway on Ayahuasca Part II; Giorgio Samorini Profiles an Italian Drug Pioneer; article on MDMA and States of Consciousness.

Issue #3: Ann Shulgin on the New Psychotherapy; a Useful Guide to *Phalaris* Grass with illustrations; an article entitled "Deadly Nightshade and Rabbits;" an article entitled "A Mycological Hypotheses."

Freakbeat Magazine

P.O. Box 1288 Dept. R
Gerrards Cross
Bucks SL9 9YB,
England.

Interviews and reviews of U.K. psychedelic bands such as The Shaman, Porcupine Tree, Viv Akauldren, Bevis Frond, Purple Overdose, Magic Mushroom Band and many more. Issue #7 + #8 have articles on Terence McKenna, Issue #8 also has an article on ayahuasca. Only issues # 5, 6, 7 and 8 are available.

Issue #5 - £ 3
Issue #6 - £ 4.50
Issue #7 - £ 5
Issue #8 - £ 5.50

Prices include postage.

"Every man takes the limits of his own field of vision for the limits of the world." - Schopenhauer

High Times

P.O. Box 410 Dept. R
Mt. Morris, IL 61054

(800) 827-0228
Website: http://www.hightimes.com

$29.95/yr - 12 issues
Back Issues: #211-present - $5/ea

With 250 issues out, *High Times* has been around since the mid '70s and is still going strong. While mostly focused on *Cannabis*, psychedelics also get mentioned regularly. Last year's "best of" issue, #17, was devoted exclusively to psychedelics. Editor Peter Gorman occasionally writes articles detailing his travels to many parts of the world to study ethnobotanicals and their use by the indigenous people. He has written about such diverse experiences as his trips to the Amazon and using ayahuasca and psychoactive snuff, to a trip to NYC to visit with the Temple of the True Inner Light and sample their sacrament DPT—a smokeable tryptamine.

Integration

(Journal for Mind Moving Plants and Culture)

Bilwis-Verlag
Eschenau #29 Dept. R
d-97478 Knetzgau, Germany

$30/issue
$75/3 issues
Published once yearly

A good looking magazine, high quality and well illustrated, I just can't bring myself to part with $75 for a subscription. I'm hoping the price will come down in the future. There are presently 4 issues out (issue 2/3 is a double issue), and all are still available. The issues are about 80 pages in length with articles in English and German and a summary in the respective other language. Among its editors is Luis Eduardo Luna, anthropologist and author of *Vegetalismo: Shamanism among the Mestizo Population of the Peruvian Amazon*, and the ex-

cellent *Ayahuasca Visions: The Religious Iconography of a Peruvian Shaman* (with paintings by Pablo Amaringo).

Issue #1: Michael Horowitz - "Just Say Know;" Gordon Wasson and "The Psychedelic Revolution;" "Plant Spirits in Ayahuasca Visions" by Peruvian painter Pablo Amaringo; "Tibetan Psycho-pharmacology;" "Cultural Patterns of the Use of *Trichocereus pachanoi* among Peruvian Curanderos."

Issue #2/3: "*Amanita muscaria* usage in Catalunya;" "The Oldest Representations of Hallucinogenic Mushrooms in the World;" "Psychoactive Mushrooms in Thailand;" "Index to the Botanical Identification and Chemical Analysis of the Known Species of the Hallucinogenic Fungi."

Issue #4: Thomas Lyttle on the "Pineal Gland and the White Light Phenomenon;" Johnny Appleseed on "Brewing Ayahuasca," using "*Phalaris* and *Desmanthus* Species as the DMT Source;" Giorgio Samorini on his "Initiation into Africa's Iboga Cult;" Manuel Torres on the "Imagery Found on Chilean Snuff Trays."

Issue #5: Luis Eduardo Luna - "Ayahuasca and Art in the Upper Amazon;" Dennis McKenna- "Bitter Brews and Other Abominations: The Uses and Abuses of Some Little-Known Hallucinogenic Plants;" Jonathan Ott - "Ayahuasca Ethnobotany, Phytochemistry and Human Pharmacology;" Richard Evans Schultes - "The Antiquity of Psychoactive Plant Use in the Americas;" "Alexander Shulgin - "The Art of Seeing;" Stacy Schaeffer - "The Crossing of the Souls: Peyote, Perception and Meaning Among the Huichol Indians of Mexico."

Issue #1 - $30
Issue #2/3 - $45
Issue #4 - $30
Issue #5 - $30

These issues are also available domestically from Mind Books.

"We fear something before we hate it." - Connolly

The Mushroom Culture
Published by

Florida Mycology Research Center
P.O. Box 8104 Dept. R
Pensacola, FL 32505

(904) 327-4378

$20 for 1 yr - 4 issues
33 back issues available at $5/ea (photocopies)
Current issue #34 - $10 (original)

This quarterly publication is the newsletter of the Independent Mushroom Grower's Network. Membership is $125, for that you get the following:

1. One year subscription to *The Mushroom Culture*.

2. The book *The Mushroom Researcher*. This book lists 358 different varieties of mushroom that have antiviral, antibiotic, anticancer and anti-aging activity.

3. Your choice of any combination of mushroom spores up to $200 value for free.

4. Their video *Fruit of the Gods*. Includes general mushroom cultivation, outdoor cultivation, collecting mushrooms in the wild, field identification of psychoactive mushrooms, mushroom poisonings and toxins, and more. This sounds good, but a friend of mine got the video and said it was so bad he sent it back for a refund. Running time 80 minutes.

5. The publication *Compounds Produced by Mushrooms and Other Fungi*. A reference book that allows you to look up a compound and find out what mushroom or fungus produces it.

6. Finally, you get "A large membership certificate suitable for framing and a personal I.D. card to carry with you in your wallet." What, no decoder ring?

You can subscribe to *The Mushroom Culture* without becoming a member, cost is $20/yr for 4 issues. There are also 33 back issues available for $5/ea. I have two of the issues, but I am not very impressed. I think they are overpriced since they are just inexpensive photocopied pages, one issue only 7 pages long. My main complaint is that the man who writes the newsletter and runs the Florida Mycology Research Center uses the publication to vent his spleen about everything from the AIDS epidemic to his mushroom cultures being intercepted by customs, to his newsletters getting wrinkled up in the mail, to even more ranting about AIDS. This leaves less room for the kind of information for which people subscribe to a mushroom newsletter in the first place. *The Mushroom Culture* reeks of the editor's attitude that it's his publication, his organization, and he can say whatever he wants no matter how self-referential and trite it is.

Peyote Awareness Journal
P.O. Box 778 Dept. R
Kearny, AZ 85237

$5 - sample issue
$25 for 1 yr (6 issues)
$35 foreign

This bi-monthly journal is put out by the Peyote Foundation (see their listing under "Organizations".) This is a new publication, the first issue came out in July '96. It's 12 pages long, with illustrations and photographs of peyote throughout.

The goal of the journal is to increase awareness of the peyote plant and its sacramental uses. Each issue will have a section devoted to cultivation tips, where readers can write in and get answers to their questions about propagation. Each issue will also have a section devoted to the medicinal use of peyote. This issue talks about the use of a peyote extract to raise the T-cell count of AIDS patients.

There is also an article detailing the legal troubles of founders Raven and Leonardo Mercado. In Oct. 1995, a SWAT team raided their residence and confiscated about 1000 living peyote plants and some dried buttons. The Mercados are not members of the Native American Church, but contended that the confiscation of their sacrament was a violation of their religious freedom. Faced with a weak case for prosecution, the charges were dropped. For three and a half months, the peyote plants remained in police custody. After much negotiation, the cacti were returned, but 40% - almost 400 plants - were ruined due to improper storage conditions. The remaining cacti were planted in a recently constructed shadehouse on the property of the Peyote Foundation.

This first issue of the *Peyote Awareness Journal* is an introduction to the founders of this organization and their beliefs. I have seen many publications start out with high hopes, say they are going to produce 4-6 issues per year, only to fall behind and publish 1-2 issues a year due to lack of funds. This is a sincere group of people, and I hope they receive enough subscriptions to be able to maintain the bi-monthly status of this publication.

Pills-A-Go-Go
**1202 E. Pike St. #849 Dept. R
Seattle, WA 98122**

$12/yr - "?" issues

Back Issues Not Available

This is the one listing in here that has nothing to do with psychedelics, but it is one of my favorite newsletters, so I had to give it a plug. *Pills-A-Go-Go* is written by and for the pharmaceutical aficionado. Its focus is pills, pain killers, tranquilizers, barbiturates, you name it. The emphasis here is on extolling the virtues of prescription drugs, hence psychedelics are almost never mentioned. Many people into entheogens do not have much of an interest in analgesics or barbiturates, but if you are an equal opportunity consumer, and like them all, then this publication will make for an interesting read. Each issue has articles, news items and letters from readers with often humorous tales of stupor and catatonia at the hands of Percodan, Valium, Demerol and the like. You will get information here you won't find anywhere else. Fearless editor Jim Hogshire has an appreciation and enthusiasm for the subject matter that is contagious. Jim has written a number of books including: *Sell Yourself to Science, You Are Going to Prison, Opium for the Masses,* and his forthcoming *Pharmaceutical Nation.* If you harbor reverential feelings towards pills and ingest them with a well-honed attitude of hedonistic appreciation, you will enjoy *Pills-A-Go-Go.*

PlantWise
**(Botanical Dimensions)
P.O. Box 807 Dept. R
Occidental, CA 95465**

**Published "Occasionally"
$20 for 4 issues,
$25 foreign airmail**

Back issues 1-4, $4/ea, issues 5-6, $5/ea

The newsletter of Botanical Dimensions. When they say published "occasionally" they mean it - the most recent issue, #6, came out in autumn '94, the previous issue came out over 2 years earlier in the spring of '92. The stated goal is "To educate, elucidate, and encourage the readership to a greater awareness of the plant world and our intimate human connection with it."

Their newsletter includes excerpts from ethnobotanical literature, book reviews, notes from those doing work out in the field, profiles of medicinal and shamanic plants, and articles by Dennis McKenna on plant chemistry and ayahuasca, a subject he is an expert on. Subscribing to *PlantWise* gives Botanical Dimensions funding for its much needed effort to preserve and study these rare medicinal plants. I'm not sure if any more issues of *PlantWise* will be coming out. If you subscribe, I suggest you request they send you issues 1-4 to fulfill your subscription.

Psychedelic Illuminations
**P.O. Box 3186 Dept. R
Fullerton, CA 92634**

714-733-1252

**E-mail: pimagazine@aol.com
Website: http://www.lycaeum.org/~pi/**

$30/4 issues ($12 overseas shipping)

Back Issues
Issue #1 - Sold out, Issue #2 - Sold out
Issue #3 - Sold out, Issue #4 - $10
Issue #5 - $8, Issue #6 - $8
Issue #7 - $9, Issue #8 - $7

I used to really like this magazine and gave it glowing reviews in previous issues of the

Continued on next page...

"Nothing is enough to the man for whom enough is too little." - Epicurus

Sourcebook. It is still a good magazine, but it has become more commercial and is trying to appeal to a wider audience, and its articles are not as cutting edge as they used to be. It takes them so long to get each issue out that much of what they report is old news by the time I read it. The most recent issue (#8) had a bit too many references to Jerry Garcia for my liking, it felt like I was reading a cross between *Relix* and *High Times*. This issue also has a four page article on how to modify your car engine to burn water, written by some angry heavy metal musician—what the hell is going on here? *PI* is losing their focus and trying to expand their readership by appealing to a wider common denominator. I think this is unfortunate.

Issue #4 - An excellent interview of ethnobotanist and explorer Peter Gorman by Thomas Lyttle (of *Psychedelic Monographs and Essays* fame); "Three Psychedelic Lessons" by Jim DeKorne, editor of the *Entheogen Review*, who relates 3 of his memorable LSD experiences; an article on vivisection; an article by Terence McKenna entitled "Imagination in the Light of Nature;" an interview with Sasha and Ann Shulgin (authors of *PIHKAL*); Rainforest Action Network Updates; "The Mafiazation of America" by Robert Anton Wilson - an article on the need to decriminalize drugs; and the chemical synthesis for DMT and DET is explicitly spelled out.

Issue #5 - An article on the Hoasca Project by Dennis McKenna and Charles Grob (the Hoasca Project studied the use of hoasca tea, or ayahuasca, by members of the Uniao do Vegetal (UDV), a Brazilian religious sect); an interview with Timothy Leary; an article reviewing psychedelic research worldwide by Rick Doblin; an overview of the events at Bicycle Day, celebrating the 50th anniversary of Albert Hofmann's discovery of LSD on April 16, 1943; an interview with Thomas Pinkson who has spent time in Peru using ayahuasca and completed an 11-year apprenticeship with Huichol Indian shamans in Mexico who use peyote; an article by mushroom authority John Allen on his encounters with *Panaeolus subbalteatus*, a psychoactive mushroom of the pacific northwest.

Issue #6 - "The Search For New Jungle Medicines" by Mark Plotkin; "Chasing the Ghost of Maria Sabina" by John Allen; an interview with Terence McKenna entitled "Glossolalia, Novelty and the Great Timestream Bifurcation;" an article on ayahuasca analogues by Jonathan Ott; a piece by Jim DeKorne entitled "The Experience Of Many Worlds" excerpted from his book *Psychedelic Shamanism*; a report on the clinical trials testing intravenous administration of DMT on 12 research subjects; an expository on the psychedelic symposium held April 28, 1994 at Chapman University in Orange, CA entitled "Gathering Of The Minds."

Issue #7 - An article detailing the synthesis of 2C-B; "Stalking the Spirit of Ibogaine" by Arjuna de Silva; "Talking Art: Imagination and Albert Hofmann" an interview of Jan Seather; "LSD and Depression" by Kimberly Wade; "High Speak" an interview with Thomas Lyttle; "Transmissions" an interview with Jonathan Ott, and more.

Issue #8 - "Fitz Hugh Ludlow-American Psychedelic Pioneer;" "Praise the Mushrooms" - an article detailing mushroom motifs in Islamic art and the psychedelic churches of Africa; "Irish Soma" - discusses entheogenic use in relation to Celtic folklore; article by Terence McKenna entitled "The Jeweled Web of Indra" about the World Wide Web; "Tripping with Captain Zip" an interview with Frasier Clark; an article by Runyon Wilde entitled "Hallucinations on the Archaic Revival" about McKenna's book *The Archaic Revival*

Psychedelic Island Views

1803 Mission St. Suite 175 Dept. R
Santa Cruz, CA 95060

E-mail: bruce@mindmedia.com
Website: http://www.island.org
(408) 427-1942
Fax (408) 426-8519

$40 - one year subscription

Vol. 1, No. 1 - $6
Vol. 1, No. 2 - $5
Vol. 1, No. 3 - $5
Vol. 2, No. 1 - N/A
Vol. 2, No. 2 - $5

This is the newsletter of the Island Group, a "Free association of individuals dedicated to the creation of a psychedelic culture." Named after Aldous Huxley's book *Island*, there have been 5 issues published so far. The editor is Bruce Eisner, author of the book - *Ecstasy: The MDMA Story.*

This newsletter has been calling itself a quarterly publication since its inception in 1991, but only one issue has appeared each year since then. The newsletter was simply called *Island Views* for its first four issues, but with the publication of the latest issue in August '96, the name is now *Psychedelic Island Views.* I imagine this is an attempt to try and compete more directly with *Psychedelic Illuminations.*

Back issues of *Island Views* were typically twenty pages long, this new issue is forty eight pages long and has a glossy magazine cover - it certainly looks more professional. This new issue is dedicated to Timothy Leary and contains an interview with him and several articles written by friends and associates. There is also a good interview of Ram Dass by the authors of the book *Mavericks Of The Mind*, and an article on the First International Conference on Drug War Prisoners by John Beresford.

This publication has always suffered from the inconsistent quality of its articles, ranging from redundant to informative. This new issue is no exception, but the articles are more consistently interesting.

If you become a member of Island Group, you get a one year subscription to *Psychedelic Island Views.* There now is no mention of how often it will be published; my guess is one or two issues a year. If you just want the magazine, individual issues are available from Xines, see their listing later in this section.

Psychedelic Resource List

- Order From -

Soma Graphics

P.O. Box 19820 Dept. R
Sacramento, CA 95819-0820

(916) 348-5206

E-mail: jonrhanna@aol.com

$16/yr, $20/foreign - quarterly resource list

The *PRL* in book form, a compilation and update of the first five issues - $19.95 + $3.00 USA, $5.00 foreign for S&H. CA residents add $1.55 for sales tax.

Various reports on growing and extraction techniques $5/ea. (see below)

This is an excellent directory which I highly recommend, particularly if you have interests in the kind of businesses they list that I don't. Contrary to its name, this directory has many listings unrelated to psychedelics. In addition to many of the businesses listed here in the *Psychedelic Sourcebook*, they also include businesses that sell indoor grow lights, hemp related products, head shops, and clothing. Their categories are - Book Vendors and Publishers, Cacti, Cultural Resources, Ethnobotanicals, Gardening and Lighting Supplies, Hemp Related, Information Sources, The Law, Merchandise and Gadgets, Mushrooms, Non-Profit and Religious Organizations, Periodicals, Posters, Radio, Stuff To Smoke, Seeds, Tapes, Videos, and Book Reviews, the Internet and more.

Soma Graphics will be publishing all five issues of the *PRL* updated and revised in book form in October '96. The supplements will still continue to be published for subscribers to the *PRL.* Even if you buy the book, you should consider subscribing so you can be kept updated about the always changing marketplace.

Soma Graphics also sells reports on growing and extraction techniques. There are 6 reports currently available:

Continued on next page...

"Any profound view of the world is mysticism." - Albert Schweitzer

1) *Potentiating the Psychedelics*
   Detailing the use of *Peganum harmala.*

2) *The Toad Report*
   Discusses the venom of *Bufo alvarius* and the pure compound 5-MeO-DMT.

3) *Simple Extraction Methods of LA-III from Argyreia and Ipomoea Species*
   Details the extraction of lysergic acid amides from baby Hawaiian woodrose and morning glory seeds.

4) *How to Grow Peyote and other Psychoactive Cacti*

5) *How to Make Ayahuasca & Smokable Tryptamines*
   Discusses *Peganum harmala* and *Phalaris* grass extraction.

6) *How to Make Yuba Gold For About $1.00 Per Ounce*
   Lists all herbs and their chemical constituents for this legal, mildly psychotropic smoking blend.

These reports are well researched.
Reports are $5 each, $10 for any three reports, or $15.00 for all six.

Talking Raven
P.O. Box 45758 Dept. R
Seattle, WA 98145

Back Issues - $3

In their own words "Iconoclastic. . . gothic. . . austere. . . *Talking Raven* defies simple categorization by destroying its own image with each and every forthcoming issue, bringing you consistent immediacy and unexpected news through the guise of essays, interviews, fiction, poetry and other dangerous, image-rich information."

Published on the equinoxes and solstices, *Talking Raven* is free on the streets of their hometown Seattle, the rest of us have to pay - but it's worth it. Some past contributors include Terence McKenna - "The Bohemian Institute of Prague" (vol. 2, #2), also "Women and Language" (vol 2, #4), and "Technomads in Hyperspace" (vol. 3, #2) The autumn equinox '94 issue was devoted to intoxication and had an interview with Jim DeKorne entitled "Ayahuasca Gardening;" also an interview with Jim Hogshire on opium; an excellent interview with Ken Adams and Britt Welin, aka Rose X Media House, on their use of psychedelics to inspire their work (they created the *Alien Dreamtime* video featuring Terence McKenna). Hakim Bey is a regular contributor as well as Rob Brezsny; plus "An unending lineage of poets and artists from around the world creating serious whimsy for the insurrection of imagination."

Talking Raven is no longer published, but most of their back issues are available. Write them for a list of their back issues, which describes the contents of each one.

TIES
P.O. Box 8104 Dept. R
Pensacola, FL 32505

$120/yr - 4 issues
$600/ lifetime membership
$750/ overseas membership

No, that is not a typo for the price of a lifetime membership in The International Entheogenic Society - they really do have the audacity to ask that much. When I asked the head of this "organization" why he was charging so much, he said it was a way to keep undesirables from becoming members. This sounds like a very elitist approach to keep law enforcement, or whoever, from seeking membership. If you know someone who is a member, then you can become a charter member for $25/yr. - but you don't know anyone who is a member, do you? So forget about qualifying for the reasonable membership fee.

Their newsletters cost $40/ea. or $25/ea. for back issues. I have the first issue; it is a whopping 6 pages long and only 3 of these pages contain text! Of the 3 pages of text, one page is taken up with self promotion, i.e. subscription rates, copyright info., back issue info., etc. Another page is taken up with a few reprinted letters, ostensibly from members, but I'm not going to trust any information on entheogens from people who are stupid enough to shell out $600 to become a member of this "society."

Finally, on the third page of text, there are 2 articles, one about extracting LSA from baby Hawaiian woodrose seeds, and the other about how to make marijuana beer. This recipe calls for 7 oz. of pot to produce 5 gallons of beer. This sounds like a real waste of weed (and beer), but if you want to contaminate 5 gallons of perfectly good beer with THC, here is the way to do it.

To top it all off, this is the only organization I know of that misspells its own name. They spell the word "entheogenic" with two "t's," so their letterhead reads "The International Entheogentic Society." I am speechless. This glaring mistake says more about the level of competency of this "organization" than anything else I could say.

Xines / Desert Moon

1226 - A Calle de Comerico Dept. R
Santa Fe, NM 87505

800-547-0182

E-Mail: xines@xines.com
Website: http://www.xines.com/xines

$4 Catalog

Xines is a distributor of alternative magazines. You can purchase single issues of some of the magazines listed in this section, so you can see if you want to subscribe. They do not carry back issues; for those you need to order direct from the magazines. If you place an order from Xines, you will receive their newsletter *Xine O Phile*, which comes out four times a year and will keep you updated on new titles.

The relevant magazines they carry are: *High Times, Psychedelic Island Views* (newsletter of the Island Group), *MAPS, Lysergic World* (great tabloid style publication all about LSD), *Pills-A-Go-Go, and Psychedelic Illuminations.*

They carry a huge array of magazines on everything from gardening to film, science fiction to sexuality, and paganism to animal rights. Recommended.

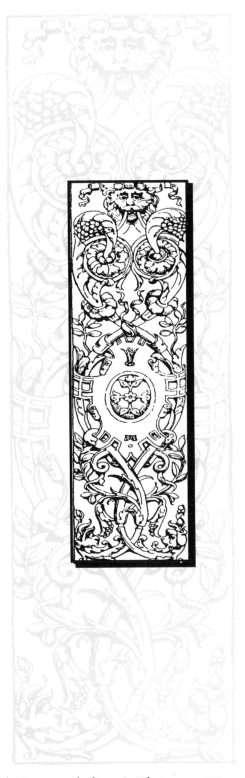

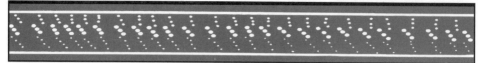

Albert Hofmann Foundation

P.O. Box 341589
Los Angeles, CA 90034

(310)281-8110

Founded in 1988 by the psychiatrist Oscar Janiger, who was one of the pioneers in LSD research during the 17 years when research was legal.

The foundation sent out a letter in 1995 announcing it was suspending its status as a membership organization, at least through 1996. Apparently, the work involved in maintaining a membership organization diverted too much energy away from their main mission - collecting and archiving information on psychedelics. The foundation used to publish a bulletin (irregularly), organize events and run a small mail order catalog offering books and tapes. All this has been put on hold for now while they concentrate on building their collection of literature and converting it to an electronic data base.

The foundation membership base had been eroding over the years, so not too many people are affected by this change. The foundation lost money in each of the last 5 years of operation, only in its first two years of business did it show a profit. Their financial problems stemmed from leasing a building they could not afford. The foundation archives are now stored in the office of John Beresford, M. D. and are not open to the public.

The foundation seems to have always suffered from disorganization and lack of funds. Their Board of Advisors reads like a who's who of researchers in the psychedelic field - but even with all this "advice," the foundation has been floundering for years.

The foundation hopes after spending 1995 and 1996 reorganizing and fund-raising, that they can reinstate membership sometime in 1997. They hope to have their website up in late '96. In the meantime, they say they will keep the public informed of their activities in the pages of M.A.P.S. newsletters in a section devoted to Foundation affairs.

Axiom

P.O. Box 190 Dept. R
Makawao, HI 96768

(800) 76-AXIOM
E-mail: axiom@aloha.net

Axiom promotes some of Terence McKenna's speaking engagements like his summer '96 "A Think Along Tour" with dates in N.Y., Colorado, New Mexico and California. They also do workshops with Michael Harner, Stanislav Grof and others. From their website: "Consciousness expansion, shamanism, psychedelic culture, creativity, sexuality, new science, spirituality, health alternatives, transpersonal psychology, and other new edge ontologies. . .Axiom. . . generating participation in advanced and transformative mind." Call or e-mail them to be put on their mailing list.

Botanical Dimensions

P.O. Box 807 Dept. R
Occidental, CA 95465

$20/yr. membership

Botanical Dimensions is a nonprofit organization dedicated to collecting and documenting medicinal and shamanic plants and surviving plant lore from cultures practicing folk medicine in the tropics worldwide.

This effort collects and preserves living plants used in traditional healing and shamanic ritual. Special attention is paid to the practices, songs and stories that accompany each species, with most work being done in Meso America and South America. BD's research and funds have helped found ethnobotanical gardens in Peru and Hawaii. A library and database are maintained to document the taxonomy, chemistry, geographical

"Out of your vulnerabilities will come your strength." - Freud

range, methods of use and cultural myths related to the origin and identity of each plant.

The newsletter, *PlantWise*, is published very sporadically and subscriptions are $20/four issues. (See listing under "Magazines and Newsletters.") BD does not sell plants or plant material, but welcomes tax-deductible contributions to fund ongoing fieldwork.

Botanical Preservation Corps
P.O. Box 1368 Dept. R
Sebastopol, CA 95473

The BPC consists of a network of travelers, mostly to tropical environments, who collect plant specimens and data which are passed on to botanical gardens. They also hold training sessions in Hawaii and Mexico with a focus on the ethnopharmacology of entheogens. These seminars offer a rare opportunity to learn techniques of botanical chemistry including field spot testing, extraction and isolation of medicinal factors, and methods of plant collecting. The BPC offers a practical, illustrated field manual which details procedures for the collection and preparation of voucher specimens and propagative material (seeds, cuttings, etc.) for $12. For more information on their seminars send them a SASE. They also sell audio tapes of their seminars featuring Terence McKenna, Jonathan Ott, Dennis McKenna, Alexander Shulgin, Richard E. Schultes and others. Highly recommended. See listing under "Audio & Video Tapes."

Council on Spiritual Practices
P.O. Box 460065 Dept. R
San Francisco, CA 94146
(415) 285-9000
FAX (415) 285-9071
E-mail: csp@csp.org
Website: http://www.csp.org/

"The Council on Spiritual Practices sponsors an electronic mail forum to facilitate entheogen-related discourse among its members. This service is provided as part of an initiative, the Entheogen Project, to enable churches and spiritual groups to use selected entheogens safely and legally in their practices and to gather knowledge about the immediate and long-term effects of such use. The entheogen 'e-mail list' works like this: A message sent by a subscriber to the Internet address - entheogen@csp.org is automatically forwarded to each of the subscribers on the list. Recipients of these messages may reply privately to the sender or may 'converse' publicly by sending replies back to entheogen@csp.org. The list is open only to members of CSP. To join, contact us by letter, fax, or e-mail to request a membership form. You will receive a private e-mail note welcoming you to the list when your completed form is processed."

The Drug Policy Foundation
4455 Connecticut Ave., NW, Suite B-500 Dept. R
Washington, DC 20008-2302
(202) 537-5005
E-mail: dpletter@dpf.org
$25 Membership ($35 foreign)
Back Issues #23-28 - $5

This organization strives to educate the public on alternatives to current drug control strategies. They try to correct inaccurate facts found in the media and present alternate policies to our current failed drug laws. Their projects include:

The Drug Policy Letter - a quarterly publication sent to government officials, the media and members of DPF. I've subscribed for the past 2 years and this is a good publication. Professional and well-written with interesting articles, it averages about 30 pages per issue.

Congressional Forums - The DPF hosts forums to educate legislators on drug policy issues.

Television - They offer a 50 part educational talk show entitled: "America's Drug Forum." This is a debate format show with experts discussing the implications of different reform options. They also have one of the most extensive video libraries of documentaries and

Continued on next page...

"That life is worth living is the most necessary of assumptions." - Santayana

related drug policy programs.

The Reformers Catalog - This is a collection of the most recent publications in the field of drug policy.

I highly recommend you become a member of the DPF. This group is well-organized and is making a valuable contribution by offering a counter balance to all the false and misleading information coming out of Washington in its terribly misguided "War on Drugs."

The Fane
Box 8179 Dept. R
Victoria, B.C.
Canada V8W 3R8

Website:http://www.
lycaeum.org/~thefane
/index.htm

$20/yr. membership
$4/current newsletter

The Fane of the *Psilocybe* Mushroom Association is a psychedelic religious organization that has been around since 1980. "The Fane is a fourth way mystical school that celebrates the mushroom sacrament as the most sublime and gracefully efficient access to the expansion of consciousness which is what we define as the religious experience. As such it functions as the integral aspect of our religious community." Membership in the Fane is open to all who agree with the three following principles.:

1. That all mushrooms of the genus *Psilocybe* are sacraments and their ingestion is a religious practice and an aid to enlightenment.

2. Everyone has the right to expand consciousness and to stimulate aesthetic, visionary, and mystical experience by whatever means one considers desirable without interference from anyone, so long as such practice does not injure another person or their property.

3. We do not encourage the ingestion of the sacrament by those who are unprepared.

Their newsletter *Sporeprint* contains mostly re-

prints of articles that have appeared in other magazines and newspapers and is not very interesting. They maintain a large library and work toward repealing Canada's drug laws. $20/year will get you on their mailing list to receive *Sporeprint*.

Fundación Yejá
P.O. Box 1004 Dept. R
El Cerrito, CA 94530
Website: http://www.ecuanex.apc.org/yeja

$5 - Catalog and registration form

This organization used to be known as Pangaean Expeditions, and before that Eco-Emissary. They are involved in rainforest conservation and the preservation of indigenous cultures.

Their focus is Ecuador, one of the smallest countries of South America but which contains the largest remaining intact wilderness on earth. Half of the world's bird species are found there—Ecuador's rainforest has served as a gene pool and seed base for the entire planet.

In addition to their various projects, Fundación Yejá sponsors workshops in the Ecuadorian Amazon twice a year. The next workshop will be held Feb. 1-15, 1997. The cost is $2,700. Space is limited to 22 people. The workshop activities include: medicinal plant identification walks through the rainforest; ethnobotanical field techniques - plant collecting and pressing; traditional healing plant ceremonies led by experienced shamans. There will be river travel by canoe as well as air travel. The itinerary is laid out in detail in the catalog.

Fundación Yejá is run by Jonathon Sparrow Miller, among others. Jonathon is a well known, self-educated ethnobotanist, conservationist, deep-ecologist. He has participated in some of the Botanical Preservation Corps' seminars on topics dealing with plant entheogens. He comes to the U.S. each fall, facilitating sessions and giving slide show presentations.

"Learning to live is learning to let go." - Sogyal Rinpoche

From Their Brochure:

"The workshops in the Amazon provide genuine intercultural exchange and learning with some of Ecuador's most progressive leaders, thinkers and activists. Participants will have a person-to-person opportunity to meet and learn from authentic forest peoples, elders, traditional healers, shamans, maestro vegetalistas and midwives. This experience is about deep ecology: reverence for nature, stewardship, abundance."

"Participate with Fundación Yejá, either by attending a workshop or by donating financial gifts (which can be tax-deducted if needed.) You will be supporting some of the most progressive and innovative Rainforest conservation approaches currently being undertaken, affecting over 3,500 Rainforest People of 5 distinct ethnic communities, living amidst 6 million or more acres of tropical Rainforest, at the headwaters of the Amazon River."

"This is important work, needs to be supported and is making a real difference." — Terence McKenna

Fungophile
P.O. Box 480503 Dept. R
Denver, CO 80248

(303) 296-9359
E-mail: art_goodtimes@infozone.org
Website:http://telluridemm.
   com/ mushroom.html

Free Brochure

Fungophile sponsors the Telluride Mushroom Conference, 4 days of seminars and celebrations of edible, psychoactive and poisonous mushrooms. The conference is held each year in August. Talks will be given on mushroom identification, cultivation on straw, medicinal mushrooms, gardening with mushrooms, and much more.

1996's featured guest speaker was Charles Grob, M.D. Dr. Grob is one of the founders of the Heffter Research Institute and is an Associate Professor of Psychiatry at the UCLA School of Medicine. He has received the first FDA approval to carry out human research with MDMA. Dr. Grob gave talks on MDMA and ayahuasca at the 1996 conference.

Returning guest speakers included Paul Stamets (author and owner of Fungi Perfecti), Andrew Weil (author of many health books and all around mushroom fanatic), John Corbin (specialist in mushroom cultivation), Gary Lincoff (author of *Audubon Field Guide to North American Mushrooms*), and Rita Rosenberg (author of *Mushroom Cookbook*).

Besides the lectures, daily hikes are held into the surrounding mountains to collect edible and poisonous species, and a mushroom "cook and taste party" is held so participants can sample the many species of edible mushrooms collected.

Registration is $235 with meals, $190 without. Vegetarian meals are available on request. There are many free campsites available about 20 minutes from Telluride. A limited number of low cost campsites are available in Telluride.

This is a great yearly conference which is also a lot of fun - highly recommended.

Heffter Research Institute
7 Avenida Vista Grande, Suite B-7 Dept. R
Santa Fe, NM 87505

(505) 820-6557
Website: http://
   www.heffter.org

Free Prospectus

This Institute is a group of physicians and pharmacologists who have joined together to promote research on psychedelic drugs. They believe this research holds more potential for producing genuine breakthroughs in understanding the human mind than any other type of research. They have not acquired their own facility yet but are soliciting funds to support research projects at other institutions for the time being. From their pamphlet - "We know that there are a myriad of possible therapeutic uses for psychedelic drugs, from the treatment of mental disorders and

Continued on next page...

addictions to improving the quality of life for the terminally ill. But, the sad fact is that so little well-designed research has been done - most of that without the advantage of the analytical technology and knowledge of brain chemistry and pharmacology available today - it will take an enormously concentrated effort to make up for the 20-30 'lost years' when research was essentially banned."

The Institute also wants to preserve the botanical knowledge of indigenous people and interpret it for use in modern culture. They aim to publish scientific reports and organize conferences to present research results from psychedelic drug research worldwide.

Two of the better-known founders of the Institute are Dennis McKenna and Charles Grob. Dennis is a chemist and ethnopharmacologist, and coauthor of *The Invisible Landscape* with his brother Terence. He is also a consultant for Nutraceutix, a natural products health care company. Charles Grob is an associate professor of psychiatry at Harbor-UCLA Medical Center and is currently doing FDA-sanctioned clinical research with MDMA on human volunteers.

The Institute has established an impressive scientific advisory board that includes most of the leading researchers in the field. They have developed a number of research projects for which they are soliciting funding. These research projects are:

1) MDMA Modification of Physical Pain and Psychological Distress in Patients with End Stage Cancer.

2) The Relationship Between Peak Experience and Outcome in LSD Assisted Psychotherapy with Substance Abusers.

3) Effects of MDMA on the Human Brain.

4) Psychobiologic Effects of MDMA in Humans.

5) Differential Effects of Hallucinogens, Entactogens, and Psychostimulants.

6) Receptor Mechanisms Contributing to Psychedelic Drug Effects.

7) A Controlled Study of the Impact of Native American Church Peyotism.

8) Chemical and Pharmacological Investigations of Centrally Active Labiates.

9) Investigations on the Human Psychopharmacology of Ayahuasca: Phase II.

10) Receptor Profiles of Lysergamides Related to LSD.

The Institute was named after Dr. Arthur Heffter, a German pharmacologist who in 1897 discovered that mescaline was the psychoactive chemical in peyote.

Island Group
**1803 Mission St. Suite 175 Dept. R
Santa Cruz, CA 95060**

**408-427-1942
E-mail: bruce@mindmedia.com
Website: http://www.island.org**

$40/yr. membership

The Island Group is "A free association of individuals dedicated to the creation of a psychedelic culture." They organized the Bridge Conference at Stanford University in Feb. '91 and helped to organize the 50th Anniversary of LSD festivities held at UC Santa Cruz in April '93. They publish *Psychedelic Island Views* "A quarterly newsletter bringing you articles, news and opinion from the cutting edge of psychedelia." The newsletter is edited by Bruce Eisner, author of *Ecstasy: The MDMA Story* - one of the better books on the subject. They also sell a small selection of audio and video tapes and books (see their listing under these headings). For those who live in Santa Cruz, they hold biweekly salons focusing on new areas of psychedelic investigation, write them for more details. General Membership is $40, which includes a one year subscription to *Psychedelic Island Views* (see listing under "Magazines and Newsletters".)

MAPS

1801 Tippah Ave. Dept. R
Charlotte, NC 28205

704-358-9830
FAX (704) 358-1650
E-mail: maps@vnet.net
Website: http://www.maps.org

$35/yr membership, $20 students or low income, $40 Complete set of back issues

"MAPS, The Multidisciplinary Association for Psychedelic Studies, is a membership-based organization working to assist psychedelic researchers around the world design, obtain governmental approval, fund, conduct and report on psychedelic research in humans. Founded in 1986 by Rick Doblin, MAPS is a nonprofit corporation funded by tax deductible donations from its members. MAPS is now focused primarily on assisting scientists to conduct human studies to generate essential information about the risks and psychotherapeutic benefits of MDMA, other psychedelics, and marijuana; with the goal of eventually gaining governmental approval for their medical uses."

MAPS also sells a few audio and video tapes and books. General membership is $35 which includes a one year subscription to their newsletter which is published quarterly. The newsletter is a bit dry and academic, but thorough. It will keep you informed on current research involving the use of Ibogaine and LSD for the treatment of substance abuse, studies determining the psychological and physiological effects of MDMA on humans, and studies exploring the use of smoked marijuana in the treatment of HIV-related wasting syndrome.

Neo-American Church

P.O. Box 3473 Dept. R
Austin, TX 78764

$30 membership

Formed in 1965 by Art Kleps, the famous acid church of the '60s is still around today, although mostly in name only. The church's bulletin - *Divine Toad Sweat* - is only rarely sent out, maybe once a year. The church conducts no activities, it's left up to the small number of members to get in touch with each other. I've been a member for three years, but it doesn't feel like I'm a member of anything.

Kleps spent some time at Millbrook with Leary and company where he formulated the 3 principles of the church, which are:

1. Everyone has the right to expand consciousness and stimulate visionary experience by whatever means he considers desirable and proper without interference from anyone.

2. The psychedelic substances are religious sacraments in that they encourage Enlightenment, which is the realization that life is a dream and the externality of relations an illusion.

3. We do not encourage the ingestion of the Greater Sacraments (such as LSD and peyote) by those who are unprepared and we define preparedness as familiarity with the Lesser Sacraments (such as hemp and nitrous oxide) and with solipsist-nihilist epistemological reasoning on such models as David Hume and Nagarjuna.

Membership in the church is $30, and you can even be ordained a Boo Hoo (member of the clergy) for no additional charge. You also receive a *Boo Hoo Bible* and a few issues of *Divine Toad Sweat* - the church's newsletter. If you do not wish to become a member, you can buy one of the books listed below. Chief Boo Hoo Art Kleps is a crotchety character, but intelligent, and his rants make good reading.

Membership - $30 - includes a copy of *Millbrook, a Narrative of the Early Years of American Psychedelianism, Recension of 1994.*

Millbrook, A True Story of the Psychedelic Movement "An autobiographical affidavit which names names, dates and places." Original 1975 tabloid edition - $500, or ring bound photocopy, book form - $29.95.

Boo Hoo Bible by Art Kleps. 218 pp. softcover. 1971 - $19.95 includes postage.

Millbrook, a Narrative of the Early Years of American Psychedelianism by Art Kleps. 222 pp. photocopied edition. 1994 - $19.95 includes postage.

"Curiosity is one of the permanent and certain characteristics of a vigorous intellect." -
Samuel Johnson

The Peyote Foundation
P.O. Box 778 Dept. R
Kearny, AZ 85237

$40 - associate membership
(includes subscription to the *Peyote Awareness Journal* and ceramic peyote button)
$100 - supporting membership
(includes subscription and ceramic mug with peyote design)

This organization was just started in May of 1996. Their goal is to increase awareness of the peyote plant and its sacramental uses. Towards this end they are involved in the following projects:

1. Publication of a bi-monthly newsletter - the *Peyote Awareness Journal* (see listing under "Magazines and Newsletters.")

2. Establish a library.

3. Build greenhouses for the propagation of peyote and develop intensive propagation methods.

4. Initiate conservation efforts for peyote in the wild.

5. Increase membership in the Foundation and create an educational facility on Foundation property.

6. Provide accurate information on peyote to scientific, religious, legal and educational organizations.

7. Establish a land trust in the plant's native habitat of Texas to insure its continued survival in the wild.

From reading their journal, they seem to be a sincere group of people with realistic goals and well thought out plans to achieve them. I like the fact that, unlike the Peyote Way Church of God, this is a non-denominational organization rather than a group of adherents to traditional Christian philosophy. They state in their journal: "We do not promote one religious sect or religion over another. We will not seek to define what a bona-fide peyotist is." This group realizes the shortage of peyote that will soon occur if the overharvesting of wild stands of the cacti by the Native American Church continues at its current rate. They have wisely focused on the importance of peyotists to be self-sufficient and grow their own sacrament.

Like the Peyote Way Church of God, the Peyote Foundation produces pottery decorated with images of the peyote plant and the native creatures of the Southwest. They offer these pieces with the different levels of membership available. They do not mention if the pottery is available separately, or if a catalog is available showing the various designs - you should inquire if interested.

This group's heart seems to be in the right place, so I would encourage you to consider becoming a member so they may continue their important work and achieve their goals.

Peyote Way Church of God
Star Route 1 Dept. R
Box 7X
Willcox, AZ 85643
Website: http://www.
   primenett.com/~idic/
   peyote.html

$20 Membership
$8 - Church Bylaws

Incorporated in 1979, the church maintains a 160 acre religious sanctuary dedicated to the sacramental use of peyote. Unlike the Native American Church, they are open to "all sincere communicants regardless of race or ancestry." They also do not have the legal protection to obtain peyote that the Native American Church does, something they hope to see changed by passage of the Religious Freedom Restoration Act. In 1994, the church enabled 46 members to go on "Spirit Walks," which consist of a 4-5 day stay at the church, fasting, and then the final day consuming 7-8 peyote buttons and spending the day alone in the nearby Galiuo mountains communing with spirit. Last year, they announced they had suspended spirit walks for the time being until they can gain legal government access to peyote.

This is a very religious organization who ascribe to the covenants of the Church of Jesus Christ

"Consciousness...is the phenomenon whereby the universe's very existence is made known."
- Roger Penrose

of Latter Day Saints. If you can look beyond all the religious references, a lot of what they preach is quite good. Membership is $20 plus $8 for a copy of the Church Bylaws. You will receive a membership card and be put on the mailing list to receive their newsletter - *The Sacred Record*. They also make their own line of pottery. Write them for a catalog of Mana pottery.

The Shaman's Apprentice Program

- Send Mail To -

Human Resources

Conservation International
1015 18th St., NW, Suite 1000 Dept. R
Washington, DC 20036

(202) 429-5660
E-mail: webmaster@conservation.org
Website: http://www.conservation.org/
cilib/jobs/job.htm#int

The goal of Shaman's Apprentice Program is to preserve the indigenous knowledge of medicinal plants and other rain forest products. They provide grants for young men and women to work with shamen and midwives to facilitate the transfer of knowledge to the next generation. Other aspects of the program include:

1) supporting the collection of plant specimens for herbaria and recording scientific descriptions in computerized ethnobotanical archives;

2) convening workshops for shamen from different tribal and cultural groups;

3) sponsoring the establishment of medicinal plant gardens for both educational and medical purposes within forest and rural communities.

Additionally, the program seeks to create ways through which indigenous people can obtain direct benefits from their knowledge about the forest, to promote viable health alternatives where Western medicine is unavailable or inaccessible, and to integrate indigenous and other rural communities into protected area management.

SISSC

c/o Museo Civico di Rovereto Dept. R
Largo S. Caterina 43
1-38068 Rovereto (TN)
Italy

$32 - Subscription to *Eleusis*

The Italian Society for the Study of the States of Consciousness archives and distributes information on entheogens and mankind's long history of attaining nonordinary states of consciousness through a wide variety of techniques. The society is headed up by Giorgio Samorini and Francesco Festi, the researchers who have done extensive studies with the *Phalaris* genus of plants that contain DMT and 5-MeO-DMT. They discovered a strain of *Phalaris aquatica* growing near Bologna, Italy, which they named AQ1. They were the first to publish a scientific report detailing the use of the *Phalaris* species in conjunction with *Peganum harmala* in a pharmahuasca experiment. This report, entitled *Ayahuasca-Like Effects Obtained with Italian Plants*, describes their self experiments and the dramatic results they obtained (report available from Rosetta).

The Society has an impressive scientific board including Albert Hofmann, Richard Evans Schultes, Luis Eduardo Luna and Jochen Gartz. The SISSC publishes *Eleusis*, a bulletin similar to the German publication *Integration*. Some of the articles in each issue of *Eleusis* are in Italian, others are in English. Two issues came out in 1995 and a third issue came out in May of 1996. If you want to check the publication out before subscribing, individual issues are available from Mind Books for $8.95 each.

ArtRock

1153 Mission St. Dept. R
San Francisco, CA 94103

Inquiries - (415) 255-7390
Orders - (800) 262-7249
Gallery Hours: 11-6 Tues-Fri, 11-5 Sat
Website: http://www.artrock.com

$3 Catalog

ArtRock sells sheets of blotter acid art signed by Timothy Leary. There are many designs to choose from including: *Mad Hatter*, *Portrait*, *Felix the Cat*, *Beavis and Butthead*, *Lips on Blue*, *Alice in Wonderland*, *Crucifixion*, *Fly in the Ointment*, *Space Migration*, *Carbon Jesus*, and *Alfred E. Pluribis Neuman*. These sheets look just like the real thing, but of course contain no LSD. The cost is $250. each. ArtRock also has an extensive collection of rock posters and t-shirts from the '60s through the '90s.

City of Tribes

3025 17th St. Dept. R
San Francisco, CA 94110

Free Price List

Small label featuring releases by Trance Mission, Young American Primitive, Daisy Glow, and others. Also, they sell the video *Alien Dreamtime*, featuring the voice of Terence McKenna and the psychedelic artwork of Rose X ($20+$4 S&H). Billboard magazine said "Enough to scare Timothy Leary straight." Recommended.

Delirium / Freakbeat

P.O. Box 1288 Dept. R
Gerrards Cross, Bucks
SL9 9YB, England

E-mail: delirium@
mail.bogo.co.uk

$2 Catalog

Mail order record store for European and American bands. Whether you are looking for Acid Rock, Ambient Rave, Space Rock, Psychedelia, Folk, Progressive or Garage.... rest assured there is something warped, distorted and brain destroying waiting for you here. Releases by Kava Kava, Magic Mushroom Band, Terence McKenna and Zuvuya, Moonflowers, Ozric Tentacles, Welcore and others.

Their releases with Terence McKenna are:

1. Terence McKenna and Zuvuya - *Dream Matrix Telemetry* - CD £10

2. T. McKenna, *Space Time Continuum* £12

3. Zuvuya with T. McKenna - *Shamania* CD £13

4. Zuvuya & T. McKenna - *Shaman I Am* 12" £7

5. John C. Lilly - *E.C.C.O.* - CD £12

Prices include postage

Drug Detection Lab

3117 Fite Circle, Suite 104
Sacramento, CA. 95827

(916) 366-3113

Charges $100 for drug identification. They won't tell you the purity of your sample, only if it is the chemical it is purported to be. Can test for MDMA, LSD, mescaline etc. Call for mail-in procedure.

Magic

395 Oak Creek, Suite 508 Dept. R
Wheeling, IL 60090

$1 Catalog

This company offers a number of products including:

The Umbrella Greenhouse

This grow chamber, when open, stands 39" tall and is 36" at the base. It is made of clear vinyl wrapped around an umbrella frame with a green vinyl floor. It has a full length zipper for easy access. When not in use it folds up to 2" x 47" and weighs less than 2 lbs. It is good for maintaining a high humidity environment for mushroom cultivation or growing *Salvia divinorum*. $39.95 + $5 S&H.

Magic Mister
Will raise the humidity level in the Umbrella Greenhouse into the 90% range. $34.95 +$5.00 S&H

Magic Grass Juicer
From the drawing in the brochure, this looks like the Miracle brand juicer sold in some health food stores. It's a hand crank model and is made out of cast-iron with stainless steel screens. It's great for extracting the juice out of *Phalaris* grass. $68 + $9 S&H.

Magic Negative Ion Generator
Helpful in reducing the level of contaminants in the production of mushrooms. Can be used with the Umbrella Greenhouse or your own mushroom growing container. Negative ions attach themselves to airborne contaminants and will be attracted to the inside walls and floor of the growing chamber. $69.95 + $5 S&H

Complete Automated Grow Chamber
Includes an Umbrella Greenhouse, water pump, water heater, negative ion generator, thermometer, 1 qt mushroom supplements and growing instructions. $99 + $9.80 S&H.

6 sterile petri dishes with agar ready for inoculation - $10 + $5 S&H

12 Petri dishes - $18.50 + $5 S&H.

McMagic
High protein food supplement for mushrooms grown on wheatstraw. Will increase yields. Use 1 qt. for 8 cubic feet of straw.
$10/qt. + $5 S&H
$30/gal. + $7.40 S&H

Inoculation Needles - $1/ea postpaid

The Phalaris Report - This report deals with the growing, extraction and use of *Phalaris* grass - $5

The Salvia Report - This report talks about the cultivation and use of *Salvia divinorum*, whose leaves can be smoked or chewed for their psychotropic effects - $5

Psychedelic Solution
33 W. 8th St., 2nd Floor V
New York, N.Y. 10011
(212) 529-2462 Tue-Sat 12-8pm

Catalog $3

This gallery has an excellent mail order catalog of concert posters from the '60s - '80s. Originals and reprints from all the big names: Mouse, Kelley, Griffin, Wilson, Moscoso, Williams, etc. They also have separate "collectors lists" with rare and one-of-a-kind items. Some list titles: Grateful Dead, Jimi Hendrix, Peter Max, Victor Moscoso, Robert Williams and more. My favorite item in the catalog is their *Cure of Souls* poster commemorating the 1988 exhibition of blotter acid art they had at their gallery. It's a beautiful 17"x26" poster showing dozens of actual blotter acid sheets with all their different designs and colors, makes you realize blotter is an art form in itself. Postcards of blotter acid art are also available. Poster - $20, postcards - $1. They also have a search service for psychedelic and rock collectibles. The gallery itself is open by appointment only.

Tech Enterprises
180 Hidden Lakes, Suite H-5 V Dept. R
Macon, GA 31204
800-293-7648
Website: http://www.magiczan.com

$1 catalog

Sells the "Coldfinger," an herbal extraction unit similar in function to the Isomerizer that was around in the late '70s. I have not seen one of these units or talked to anyone who has used one, so I can only quote from their catalog.

Coldfinger features:

• Makes medicinal extracts and pure essential oils.

• Home and commercial scale units available.

• All pyrex glass construction.

• Operates efficiently at all temperatures - from very low for temperature sensitive herbs to very high for difficult extractions.

Continued on next page...

"There is only one corner of the universe you can be certain of improving and that's your own self." - Aldous Huxley

- Utilizes a wide range of solvents.
- Guaranteed to extract all of the desired constituents from any herb if used properly.
- Very easy to clean and sterilize.

The Coldfinger units are superior to similar equipment available from Lab supply companies because they operate at much lower temperatures and they process much larger amounts of material. The Coldfinger's inverted condenser makes it possible to operate at lower temperatures because the solvent vapors only have to rise a short distance before they recondense and drip through the herb.

Coldfinger Home Unit

The Coldfinger Home Unit is elegant in its simplicity. This small self contained unit takes less than 5 minutes to set up and can extract 2-4

oz. of herb at a time. It can use an electric stove- top range or hotplate as a heat source. $225.

Coldfinger Commercial Unit

The Coldfinger Commercial Unit is ideal for the professional herbalist. The high capacity soxhlet basket will hold up to one half pound of ground herb

for extraction. The extra long inverted condenser provides a heavy flow of solvent to speed your extraction process. The heating unit provides pinpoint temperature control and a warm air convection current that wraps around the whole unit providing the ideal environment for solvent evaporation and condensation. Can be adapted for vacuum distillation and vacuum drying of extracts. $1,100.

Thomas Lyttle & Associates
2480 Lakeview Dr. #9 Dept. R
Naples, FL 33962

Thomas Lyttle, the publisher of the *Psychedelic Monographs & Essays* series, has been involved with LSD blotter art for a number of years. He is now offering sheets of blotter paper (minus the LSD) signed by the likes of Timothy Leary, William Burroughs, Ken Kesey, Robert Anton Wilson, Alexander Shulgin and John Lilly.

These sheets are similar to the 100 dose sheets sold on the black market, but these measure 7" square. I have seen the John Lilly sheet and it is a beautiful full color fractal design. The following sheets are currently available:

Timothy Leary Sheets

1) Geisha (900 doses)

2) Lightning Bolts

3) Oriental Crests

4) Swirling Fractals

Alexander Shulgin - Miathuna Couples
Robert Anton Wilson - Opium Den
Ken Kesey - Swirling Fractals
John Lilly - Fractal

The Leary sheets are $150/ea. but will undoubtedly go up in price since his death. All other sheets are $100/ea. All designs are in color. Write for current prices.

If you don't order anything else, you should order these catalogs and newsletters. They are the best in their respective fields.

"Sleep, riches, and health, to be truly enjoyed, must be interrupted." - Jean Paul Richter

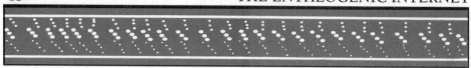

Author's Note

Welcome to the World Wide Web! As you will find, the Internet is home to an unbelievably rich collection of entheogen-related information, and this is a list of some of the most valuable resources I've found in cyberspace on the topic. There is one thing I would like to make quite clear at the start: this is not intended to be a complete list; that would require a separate book of its own. However, herein lies the beauty of the web: you can access nearly everything else out there on the subject and related topics by following the hypertext links (highlighted sections of text that one can click on with a mouse to access other web pages) contained within these sites. Happy surfing!

Businesses in the Sourcebook:

Books and Tapes:

Atomic Books
http://www.atomicbooks.com/

Last Gasp
http://www.woof.com/last_gasp.html

Mind Books
http://www.promind.com

Sound Photosynthesis
http://www.photosynthesis.com/home.html

Botanicals:

Ho Ti Products
http://www.ilhawaii.net:80/~hoti/

Kava Kauai
http://www.kauaisource.com

LER (Legendary Ethnobotanical Resources)
http://www.shadow.net/~heruka

Mycological Supplies:

Fungi Perfecti
http://www.halcyon.com/mycomed/fppage.html

Psylocybe Fanaticus E-mail address
pf@pf.seanet.com
http://www.fanaticus.com/

Publications:

Blue Water Publishing
http://www.bluewaterp.com/~bcrissey

bOING bOING
http://www.well.com/user/mark/index.html

The Entheogen Law Reporter
http://www.cyberverse.com/~martins/TELR/

Entheogen Review
http://www.cyberverse.com/~martins/TELR/er.html

High Times
http://www.hightimes.com/~hightimes/welcome.html

Journal of Psychoactive Drugs
http://www.mind.net/cns/jpd.htm

***Magical Blend* On-Line**
http://www.eden.com/magical/main.html

Robert Anton Wilson's *Trajectories* Home Page
http://www.nets.com/site/raw/trajectories.html

Drug Policy:

Drug Education Page
http://www.magic.mb.ca/~lampi/new_drugs.html

A collection of information on the socio political aspects of substance use in a variety of cultures.

Drug Reform Coordination Network On-Line Drug Policy Library
http://www.druglibrary.org/

Want specific data on just how screwed up our nation's current drug policy is? Visit this site for the cold hard facts in abundance, along with enlightening perspectives on how the rest of the world handles it. Some info. on specific materials as well.

Ethnobotanical/ Phytochemical Databases:

Herbweb
http://www.herbweb.com/

An extensive listing of plants with ethnobotanical value. Also contains a very creative multimedia "book" about tryptamines.

National Agricultural Library
http://probe.nalusda.gov:8300/index.html

Features databases covering phytochemistry, medicinal and food plants of Native America, and worldwide plant uses, among other topics.

General Information:

The Deoxyribonucleic Hyperdimension
http://deoxy.org/deoxy.htm

One of my favorite examples of the beauty of multimedia, with seamless integration of hypertext, eye-popping graphics, audio clips, and animation by Dimitri Novus, web-weaver extraordinaire. Pages on McKenna, Lilly, Leary/RAW, Gracie and Zarkov, Alan Watts, shamanism and plenty of multidisciplinary, cross-cultural info applicable to the entheogenic path.

Disembodied Eyes
http://www.cnw.com/~neuro/gaz/

A great general information repository for all of the major classes of entheogens, with an emphasis on the botanicals. Lots of data on cultivation, extraction and usage of diverse plant species and chemicals, plus many rare articles and papers in hypertext.

Hyperreal Drugs Archive
http://hyperreal.com/drugs/

Home of the archives of the late usenet newsgroup alt.drugs. The quality of on-line discussion on usenet drug channels has sadly declined (luckily, there are other options; see "Mailing Lists"), but the archives are packed with information on a variety of consciousness altering substances nonetheless.

Hyperspace
http://deoxy.org/hyper.htm

Dimitri strikes again! An astounding co-mapping of quantum physics, celtic mythology, vedic philosophy, psychic phenomena, tantra, and tryptamines, served up with style and panache to spare.

The Lycaeum Drug Archives
http://www.lycaeum.org/drugs/

The most complete and well-organized archive of information on visionary substances that I've been able to find so far. Includes a fascinating collection of trip stories collection.

Lux Illuminati
http://www.lycaeum.org/~lux/

An impressive multimedia presentation by *Psychedelic Illuminations* magazine's James Kent that is concerned with "the metaphysical manipulation of reality and all of its inner related meta-realities, pseudo-realities, virtual-realities, and hyper-realities."

Mind Warp
http://www.clas.ufl.edu/anthro/noetics/mindwarp.html

Concerned with "all things noetic (relating to consciousness)," this page contains a relatively small amount of drug data and two McKenna excerpts, but is a rich source for education on a host of closely related subjects such as cyberspace, memetics, and techno-shamanism, to name but a few.

Paranoia Drug Information Server
http://www.paranoia.com/drugs/

Information on all of the usual suspects, drawn mostly from USENET postings.

Psychedelic Abstracts On-Line
http://cyberverse.com/~martins/L4/L4.cgi?searchable

The ultimate entheogen-related database/search engine with a scope so vast it's dizzying to contemplate. If you can't find it here, you're probably S.O.L..

Psychoactives Archive
http://www.paranoia.com/~debaser/

David Laurence's well organized archives.

Sputnik Drug Information Zone
http://www.nepenthes.xo.com/

All the major players are represented here, along with good chemistry data and some cool articles unavailable elsewhere.

Literature:

(alphabetical by author when listed)

Dana Beal & Paul De Rienzo's *The Ibogaine Story*
http://www.cures-not-wars.org/ibogaine

A book in hypertext detailing a project to treat heroin addiction with ibogaine. Carlos Castaneda: see "Personalities"

Drug Culture Throughout History
http://www.paranoia.com/~foucault/Babel/

An excellent collection of drug literature drawing from such diverse sources as the *Old Testament*, the *Arabian Nights*, Arthur Conan Doyle, and Sigmund Freud.

Todd Brendan Fahey's *Wisdom's Maw*
http://www.ucs.usl.edu/~tbf4931/Wisdom/

Advertisement and excerpt from a new novel mixing fact and speculation based on government involvement in LSD research.

Gracie & Zarkov's *Notes From Underground*
http://www.deoxy.org/gz.htm

The legendary Bay Area psychonauts share the fruits of their exploration in a hypertext version of their underground classic.

The Lycaeum: Books
http://www.lycaeum.org/books/
Links to entheogenic books available on-line, book reviews of entheogenic titles by Lycaeum members and on-line book companies.

Greg Hill and Kerry Thornley's *Principia Discordia*
http://www.cs.cmu.edu/~tilt/principia/

The text that spawned the funniest cult I ever heard of.

Albert Hofmann's *LSD: My Problem Child*
http://www.paranoia.com/drugs/psychedelics/lsd/probchild

The man responsible for the isolation of psilocybin, and the bicycle ride that changed history, tells it in his own words. Translated by Jonathan Ott.

Aldous Huxley's *Doors of Perception*
http://www.cnw.com/~neuro/gaz/fresh/doors.htm

The watershed work that brought mescaline into the public eye.

Art Kleps' *MILLBROOK: A Narrative of the Early Years of American Psychedelianism*
http://www.hyperreal.com/drugs/millbrook/index.html

Find out what Leary's NY state commune was like on the inside from somebody who was there.

The Psychedelic Experience
http://www.glg.ed.ac.uk/~jfk/Docs/tibetan.html

The seminal work by the Harvard trinity, Leary, Alpert, and Metzner, that co-maps entheogenesis with the *Tibetan Book of the Dead*.

Lee and Shlain's *Acid Dreams*, Chapter One
http://hyperreal.com/drugs/psychedelics/lsd/acid.dreams

Find out everything you never wanted to know about US government involvement in the early days of the psychedelic revolution.

John Lilly's *Programming and Meta - programming in the Human Biocomputer*
http://www.city-net.com/~mbt/pamithb.html

Public edition of a report originally written for the government on altering belief structures with LSD, sensory deprivation, and the creative power of the human mind.

The Fitz Hugh Ludlow Hypertext Library
http://www.nepenthes.xo.com/Ludlow/index.html

An impressive collection of works by and about the *Cannabis* pioneer and many other classic hemp-related texts. Also contains classic essays by Theophile Gautier on hashish and Havelock Ellis on mescaline.

Terence McKenna: See "Personalities"

Excerpts from Jonathan Ott's *Ayahuasca Analogues*
http://ezinfo.ucs.indiana.edu/~rhasting/hoasca.html

Some useful tables for making ayahuasca, but no substitute for the whole book.

Proemium from Ott's *Pharmacotheon*
http://hyperreal.com/drugs/proemium/index.html

The introduction to Ott's masterwork. An

articulate, reasoned, and passionate cry for a sensible drug policy.

Nicholas Saunders' *E for Ecstasy*
http://ecstasy.org/

The most well-researched book I've seen yet on the topic.

Part II of the Shulgins' *PIHKAL*
http://www.hyperreal.com/drugs/pihkal

Synthesis instructions, dosage range, extensions and commentary on the master chemist's 170-plus creations in the phenethylamine family. However, it unfortunately lacks the first half of the work, a rich and illuminating novel that basically amounts to a thinly veiled autobiography of the first family of psychedelic psychopharmacology.

R. Gordon Wasson, Albert Hofmann and Carl Ruck's *The Road to Eleusis.*
http://www.calyx.net/~schaffer/lsd/eleucont.html

A landmark multidisciplinary effort that offers convincing evidence that the ancient Greeks used ergotized rye to brew an entheogenic potion that was at the center of the Eleusinian Mysteries.

Alan Watts' *Joyous Cosmology*
http://www.calyx.net/~schaffer/lsd/jccontnt.html

The philosopher/scholar details his "adventures in the chemistry of consciousness."

Robert Anton Wilson: See "Personalities"

The World Wide Web Psychedelic Bibliography
http://www.maps.org/wwwbib/index.html

A highly useful search engine for bibliographical data on the topic.

Mailing Lists:

CSP Entheogen List

Mostly devoted to relatively mature discussions of the sociopolitical, philosophical, and spiritual aspects of entheogens, without a lot of noise in the circuit. Definitely **not** the place to go for hardcore trip stories or potion recipes. E-mail moderator Robert Jesse at bob@csp.org for more info.

Secret Leri Home Page
http://www.leri.org/LeriWeb.html

Home page of the Leri-L Metaprogrammers Mail Service, a temporary autonomous zone in cyberspace dedicated to consciousness, philosophy, and all sorts of topics that should be of interest to you if you've bothered to read this book. Make your own judgements about the discussion on the list, but the web page is an artfully realized and often hilarious cornucopia of useful information. Don't miss the great links!

Mind Space Central
http://sage.macc.wisc.edu/~jburris/mindspace

Gallery and archive of the Mind Space mailing list, a relatively low-traffic discussion group that covers mystical territory of all sorts. Worth visiting just to see their logo artwork.

The Lycaeum
http://www.lycaeum.org/

The home to a variety of entheogen-related lists including the current jewel in the crown of the entheogenic internet, the Visionary Plants List. The site is a fountainhead of invaluable information on the subject, but the best stuff is for members only... so do yourself a favor and apply, already! If you're interested in the topic and own a computer, drop what you're doing and visit this page now!

Organizations:

Albert Hofmann Foundation
http://www.maps.org/news-letters/v6n1/06145ahf.html

A small page from the MAPS site with info. on the Foundation's plans.

Axiom
http://www.aloha.net/~axiom

Council on Spiritual Practices
http://www.csp.org/

Website features an inspiring collection of writings on many different aspects of spirituality, with a special emphasis on traditional usage of botanical and chemical agents in the exercise of religious freedom.

Drug Enforcement Agency
http://www.usdoj.gov/dea/deahome.html

Know your enemy.

Fundación Yejá
http://www.ecuanex.apc.org/pangean/secoya.html

Learn about ethnobotanist Jonathon Sparrow Miller's foundation and its plans to help empower rainforest peoples and preserve their homeland.

Heffter Research Institute
http://www.heffter.org/

Find out details about the Institute's current projects at their website. Also contains some beautiful GIF images of drug molecules that make great pinups if you have a color printer. Some people have the supermodel of the month hanging on their walls; I have these...

Island Web
http://www.island.org/

Features the *Island Views Electro-Zine*, a hypertext teaser that offers several worthwhile articles from their full length print magazine, plus a page of commentary on Huxley's classic *Island*. Their marketplace has audio and video samples of Leary, Eisner, and the Bicycle Day Conference available for free download - check it out!

Multidisciplinary Association for Psychedelic Studies
http://www.maps.org/

Complete hypertext versions of all MAPS newsletters, notices of upcoming psychedelic conferences, the WWW on-line psychedelic bibliography, medical marijuana info., and an art gallery that is not to be missed!

Temple of the True Inner Light
http://mindvox.phantom.com/~psychede/

Cyberspace home of the New York City storefront temple "that believes that psychedelics, (DPT, Marijuana, LSD, Peyote, Psilocybin, DMT, etc.), are the true Flesh of God." Contains some quite worthwhile information on alternative therapies for depression alongside the Temple's unique synthesis of psychedelia and Judeo-Christian theology.

Personalities:

Unofficial William Burroughs, Homepage
http://www.peg.apc.org/~firehorse/wsb/wsb.html

Excerpts from his work, a FAQ, pictures, and interviews with the man that apparently nothing can kill.

Carlos Castaneda Archives
ftp://ftp.earth.com/pub/archive/cc/

Features an overview of the man and his work, bibliography, commentary, and the Castaneda mailing list archives.

Soma Web's Aldous Huxley Site
http://www.primenet.com/~matthew/huxmain.html

A short bio., commentary, and some good links.

Timothy Leary Home Page
http://www.leary.com/

Tour the good doctor's virtual home via one of the more inventive user interfaces I've seen yet on the WWW. Look through his photo collection! Read excerpts from his body of work! Enjoy a VR movie of his patio! Rap with fellow visitors in the chat room! Find out what his daily drug intake during his final days was from the health report! And much, much more...

Dimitri's Timothy Leary and Robert Anton Wilson Show
http://www.deoxy.org/learyraw.htm

Everything you ever wanted to know about these two, including articles, bibliography, excerpts, interviews, photos, and links.

John Lilly Home Page
http://www.rain.org/~lili/DrJohnLilly/

Nice graphics, a bibliography, a good page on ECCO, and audio clips.

Dimitri's John Lilly Page
http://www.deoxy.org/lilly.htm

A relatively small page with links to hypertext Lilly, and a cool dolphin audio sample.

"They will say that you are on the wrong road, if it is your own." - Antonio Porchia

Terence McKenna's Alchemical Garden at the Edge of Time
http://www.levity.com/eschaton/index.html

Terence turns his imagination inside out so that we may stroll through it like a virtual museum. Information and pointers to everything you'd expect and a whole lot more, with quite remarkable graphic displays. A must.

Dimitri's Terence McKenna Land
http://www.deoxy.org/mckenna.htm

A multimedia McKenna anthology comprised of hypertext transcriptions from his lectures and writings, audio clips, and tryptaminesque visuals.

Jonathan Ott Page
http://student.uq.edu.au/~s332168/jott.htm

A small page that is still under construction as we go to press, with bio., bibliography, and a very incomplete list of entheogenic drugs.

Shulgin Trust Fund Page
http://www.hyperreal.com/drugs/pihkal/fund.html

Help the Shulgins pay off their DEA fine. If you've ever enjoyed one of his creations, it's only fair...

Unofficial Robert Anton Wilson Page
http://www.tcp.com/~prime8/raw

More than your average author's web page, including the obligatory book excerpts plus rare articles, letters to editors of various Santa Cruz newspapers, and "three misprints, several buried jokes, and one outright lie."

Dimitri's Alan Watts Page
http://www.deoxy.org/watts.htm

Great audio clips, bibliography, essays, lectures, and links.

Shamanism:

Dimitri's Shamanism Page
http://www.deoxy.org/shaman.htm

Typical Dimitri: creative and comprehensive, with lots of ayahuasca info.

Nierica - The Sacred Doorway
http://www.aonet.com/nierica/default.html

Not as much info specific to psychedelic shamanism, but good academic background material and lovely graphic design.

Specific Materials:

The alt.drugs F(requently) A(sked) Q(uestion)s
http://hyperreal.com/drugs/faqs/index.html

Tons of info. on a plethora of materials. Remember to verify what you read before acting upon it (not that I'd endorse acting upon it, mind you), - this stuff comes from usenet postings, not always the most accurate source.

Daniel Siebert's *Salvia divinorum* Pages
http://www.geocities.com/Paris/1074/salvia.html

A treasure-trove of information on the entheogenic Mexican mint, compiled by the discoverer of salvinorin A's psychoactive effects. Also, cultivation tips, sources for *Salvia*, photos and more.

The DXM FAQ
http://www.frognet.net/dxm/

Read this and snicker no more when you hear about "robo;" apparently it's quite a powerful dissociative, capable at sufficient doses of inducing ketamine-like mental states! Thorough, clear and incredibly well-researched, with a very valuable section on receptor function and neuropharmacology.

ecstasy.org
http://ecstasy.org/

Home of Briton Nicholas Saunders, author of *E for Ecstasy* and the new *Ecstasy and the Dance Culture*. Hypertext articles, all of *E for Ecstasy*, and important info on purity and safe use.

Fungi Perfecti's Mushroom Information Center
http://www.halcyon.com/mycomed/info.html

A plethora of useful tidbits for mycophiles of all kinds. Features a breathtaking photo gallery of luscious *Psilocybes*.

Gabber Net XTC info.
http://www.il.ft.hse.nl/~gabber/xtc/index.html

A good collection of useful information on

Continued on next page...

"The most exhausting thing in life is being insincere." - Anne Morrow Lindbergh

the world's most popular empathogen. Features a FAQ, synthesis info., health risks, and material on other popular club-scene drugs.

Chemical Experiences of a Hyperspatial Nature

http://www.deoxy.org/hyper.htm#cehn

This part of Dimitri's domain is the best collection of DMT related material I've found yet on the web.

The Ibogaine Dossier

http://www.desk.nl/~ibogaine

Contains several clinical articles on treatment of drug addiction with Africa's native entheogen.

Kava Home Page

http://www.prairienet.org/~kagan/kavabib.html

All the important information on the psychotropic shrub of the Pacific.

The Ketamine Konundrum

http://www.lycaeum.org/~lux/alchem/konun.htm

This section of James Kent's Lux Illuminati site is an extremely well-written, illuminating presentation on the Dom Perignon of dissociatives.

Just Say N_2O

http://www.resort.com/~banshee/Info/N2O/N2O.html

How to use nitrous with relative safety and effectiveness.

Orfeo: A dialogue between Terence McKenna & Robert Hunter

http://www.levity.com/orfeo/index.html

The Grateful Dead lyricist corresponds with Terence about the revelations of the DMT flash. Highly recommended.

Psychedelic Tryptamines

http://barroom.visionsystems.com/serendipity/trypt.html

This section of Timewave Zero software programmer Peter Meyer's Serendipity site is an information compendium of mushroom and DMT related material.

The San Pedro Fanatic Page

http://members.gnn.com/iamklaus/sanpedro.htm

"An abundance of essential information about sacramental cacti of all types."

Tryptamines

http://www2.best.com/~timj/tryptamines/0.htm

This part of the Herbweb website is a very creatively rendered multimedia "book" in hypertext on the subject of mushrooms, ayahuasca, and DMT.

Usenet Newsgroups:

For a higher signal to noise ratio, I'd recommend perusing the "Mailing Lists" section (especially the Visionary Plants Lycaeum). However, the following usenet newsgroups do exist:

alt.consciousness
alt.drugs
alt.drugs.chemistry
alt.drugs.culture
alt.drugs.pot
alt.hemp
rec.drugs.*Cannabis*
rec.drugs.misc
rec.drugs.psychedelic
sci.med
sci.med.pharmacy
sci.med.psychobiology
talk.politics.drugs

*"Jealousy, that dragon that slays love under the pretense of keeping it alive." -
Havelock Ellis*

Miscellaneous:

Analytical Services, Inc.
http://www.sims.net/drugtest/

Have your urine tested before someone else does!

Changes Home Page
http://www.icenine.com/changes/

Dedicated to consciousness and the Haight-Ashbury culture, this page is curated by Elizabeth Gips, psychedelic elder stateswoman and host of the radio show of the same name.

The Donut Hole
http://www.cat.net/~donut

Sorry, but I couldn't resist throwing this one in. My own little corner of the web contains, among other things, a hypertext version of this very document. If you don't feel like typing in all of these URLs by hand, this should be very useful.

Dope Fiends
http://execpc.com/~daanes/dopefiends.html

A nice collection of info. regarding the unfortunate social stigma faced by drug users.

The Electric Gallery
http://www.egallery.com/pablo.html

Gasp at the beauty of the ayahuasca-influenced paintings of Amazonian shaman Pablo Amaringo.

Electrum Magicum
http://www.levity.com/dimitri/index.htm

Have you met the elves yet? Either way, visit this page and see how they (and other forces) manifest to Dimitri.

Fractal Pictures & Animations
http://www.cnam.fr/fractals.html

An enormous collection of the trippy imagery that has forever blurred the boundaries between math, science, and art.

Huichol Art Center
http://www.leonardo.net/huicholart/index.html

A lovely selection of Huichol yarn paintings.

Lick This Screen
http://www.hyperreal.com/drugs/psychedelics/lsd/lick.this.screen.html

The best of blotter art for your viewing pleasure.

Melatonin FAQ
http://www.teleport.com/~jor/

Answers all of your questions about the "other" pineal secretion.

Pangaean Expeditions Home Page
http://www.ecuanex.apc.org/pangean/index.html

Find out about ethnobotanist Jonathon Sparrow Miller's Amazon workshop on plants as teachers and rainforest conservation. A cut above the average ayahuasca tourist voyage.

The Web of Possibilities
http://www.well.com/user/dpd/webposse.html

A small page with recommended reading, links and philosophy.

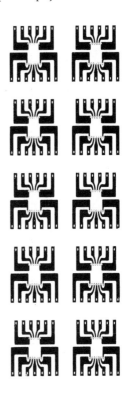

BOTANICAL NAME	COMMON NAME	MAIN ALKALOIDS
Acacia (various species)	Acacia	DMT
Acorus calamus	Sweet flag	A-asarone
Amanita muscaria	Fly agaric	Ibotenic Acid, Muscimole
Areca catechu	Betel nut	Arecoline
Argyreia nervosa	baby Hawaiian woodrose	Lysergic Acid Amides
Artemisia absinthum	Absinthe	Thujone
Arundo donax	Giant reed	DMT
Atropa belladonna	Deadly nightshade	Hyoscyamine, Scopolamine
Banisteriopsis caapi	Yajé vine, Ayahuasca	Harmine, Harmaline
Brugmansia (var. spec.)	Datura	Scopolamine
Bufo alvarius venom	Toad venom	5-MeO-DMT, Bufotenine
Calea zacatechichi	Dream herb	Unknown
Catha edulis	Khat	Cathine, Cathinone
Yohimbe	Yohimbe	Corynanthe, Yohimbine, Corynanthine
Datura stramonium	Jimson weed	Hyoscyamine, Scopolamine
Desmanthus illinoensis	Illinois bundleflower	DMT
Ephedra sinensis	Ma Huang	Ephedrine
Heimia salicifolia	Sun opener, Sinicuichi	Cryogenine
Hyoscyamus niger	Henbane	Hyoscyamine, Scopolamine
Paraguayensis	Yerba mate	Caffeine
Ipomoea violacea	Morning glory	Lysergic Acid Amides
Lophophora williamsii	Peyote	Mescaline
Nicotiana (various spec.)	Tobacco	Nicotine
Papaver somniferum	Poppy	Opium
Passiflora	Passionflower	Harmine, Harmaline
Paullinia cupana	Guarana	Guaranine, Xanthine
Peganum harmala	Syrian rue/esphand/esfand	Harmine, Harmaline
Phalaris arundinacea	Reed canary grass	DMT, 5-MeO-DMT
Piper methysticum	Kava kava	Methysticin, Kawain
Psilocybe cubensis	Magic mushrooms	Psilocybin, Psilocin
Psilocybe mexicana	Teonanácatl	Psilocybin, Psilocin
Psilocybe semilanceata	Liberty cap	Psilocybin, Psilocin
Psilocybe cyanescens	Wavy cap	Psilocybin, Psilocin
Psychotria viridis	Chacruna	DMT
Rivea corymbosa	Ololiuhqui	Lysergic Acid Amides
Salvia divinorum	Ska pastora, Pipiltzintzintli	Salvinorin A
Tabernanthe iboga	Iboga	Ibogaine
Theobroma cacao	Chocolate	Theobromine, Caffeine
Trichocereus pachanoi	San pedro Cactus	Mescaline

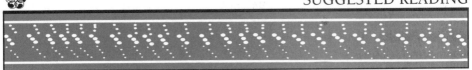

While there are many good books on psychedelics, the following are my personal favorites that I consider essential reading. The more you bring to the experience, the more you will get out of it.

Acid Dreams - Martin Lee and Bruce Shlain. New York: Grove Weidenfeld, 1985

Ayahuasca Visions: The Religious Iconography of a Peruvian Shaman - Luis Eduardo Luna and Pablo Amaringo. Berkeley: North Atlantic Books, 1991

Ayahuasca Analogues - Jonathan Ott. Kennewick, WA: Natural Prod. Co., 1994

Cosmic Trigger - Robert Anton Wilson. Berkeley, CA: And/Or Press, 1977

Drug Identification Bible - Tim Marnell - ed Denver: Drug Identification Bible, 1993

Food of the Gods - Terence McKenna, New York: Bantam Books, 1992

Gateway to Inner Space - Christian Ratsch. Prism Unity Press, 1989

Growing Gourmet and Medicinal Mushrooms - Paul Stamets. Berkeley: Ten Speed Press, 1993.

Hallucinogens and Shamanism - Michael Harner. Oxford University Press, 1973

Hallucinogens and Culture - Perter Furst. San Francisco: Chandler and Sharp, 1978

Hallucinogens: Cross-Cultural Perspectives - M. Dobkin De Rios. Prism Unity Press, 1990

Heaven and Hell - Aldous Huxley. London: Chatto and Windus, 1956.

High Priest - Timothy Leary. New York: College Notes and Texts, 1970

LSD: My Problem Child - Albert Hofmann. Los Angeles: Tarcher, 1983

Millbrook - Art Kleps. Oakland: Bench Press, 1975

Moksha: Writings on Psychedelics and the Visionary Experience - Aldous Huxley. Michael Horowitz & Cynthia Palmer, eds. New York: Stonehill, 1977

Mysterium Coniunctionis - C.G. Jung. New York: Pantheon, 1963

Notes From Underground - Gracie and Zarkov. Rosetta books, Berkeley: 1985

Persephone's Quest: Entheogens and the Origins of Religion - R. Gordon Wasson. New Haven: Yale University Press, 1986

Pharmacotheon - Jonathan Ott. Kennewick, Wa: Natural Products Co., 1993

Pharmako/Poeia - Dale Pendell. San Francisco. Mercury House, 1995

PIHKAL - Ann & Alexander Shulgin. Berkeley: Transform Press, 1991

Plants of the Gods - Richard Evans Schultes and Albert Hofmann. Vermont: Healing Arts Press, 1992

Continued on next page...

"Man's loneliness is but his fear of life." - Eugene O'Neill

Psilocybin: Magic Mushroom Grower's Guide - O.T. Oss and O.N. Oeric. Berkeley, CA: And/OR Press, 1976, rev. 1986

Psychedelic Drugs Revisited - Lester Grinspoon and James Bakalar. New York: Basic Books, 1979

Psychedelics Encyclopedia - Peter Stafford. Berkeley: Ronin Press, 1992

Psychedelic Monographs and Essays Vol 1-6, Thomas Lyttle, ed PM&E Pub Group

Psychedelic Shamanism - Jim DeKorne. Port Townsend, WA: Loompanics Unlimited, 1994

Realms of the Human Unconscious - Stanislav Grof. London: Souvenir Press, 1993 (originally published in 1975)

Thanatos to Eros - Myron Stolaroff. Berlin, Germany: VWB, 1994

The Age of Entheogens & The Angels' Dictionary - Jonathan Ott. Kennewick, WA. Natural Products Co., 1995.

The Archaic Revival - Terence McKenna. San Francisco: Harper San Francisco, 1991

The Doors of Perception - Aldous Huxley. New York: Harper, 1954

The Essential Psychedelic Guide - D.M. Turner. San Francisco: Panther Press, 1994

The Invisible Landscape - Terence & Dennis McKenna. NY: Seabury Press, 1975

The Healing Journey: New Approaches to Consciousness - Claudio Naranjo. New York: Ballantine, 1973

The Boo Hoo Bible - Art Kleps. San Cristobal, NM: Toad Books, 1971

The Mushroom Cultivator - P. Stamets & J.S. Chilton. Olympia, WA: Agarkon Press, 1983

The Politics of Ecstasy - Timothy Leary. New York: Putnams, 1968

The Yage Letters - William Burroughs and Allen Ginsberg, San Francisco: City Lights Books, 1963

True Hallucinations - Terence McKenna. San Francisco: Harper San Francisco, 1993

Wizard of the Upper Amazon - F. Bruce Lamb. Berkeley: N. Atlantic Books, 1971

"To die for a religion is easier than to live it absolutely." - Jorge Luis Borges

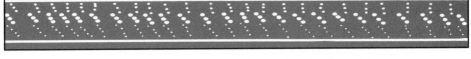

Key to Abbreaviations

SP - Spores and Kits

SG - Spore Germination

BK - Book Catalogs

T - Tape Catalogs

BT - Botanicals

SD - Seeds

M - Magazines

O - Organizations

MS - Miscellaneous

"The lust for comfort, that stealthy thing that enters the house a guest, and then becomes a host, and then a master." - Kahlil Gibran

71

"I never forget a face, but I'll make an exception in your case" - Groucho Marx